MAN'S CONQUEST OF SPACE

BY WILLIAM R. SHELTON

Foreword by James E. Webb
*Administrator, National Aeronautics
and Space Administration,
and Member of the Society's Board of Trustees*

PREPARED BY NATIONAL GEOGRAPHIC
SPECIAL PUBLICATIONS DIVISION
Robert L. Breeden, Chief

NATIONAL GEOGRAPHIC SOCIETY
WASHINGTON, D.C.

*Melvin M. Payne, President
Melville Bell Grosvenor, Editor-in-Chief
Frederick G. Vosburgh, Editor*

Man's Conquest of Space

By William R. Shelton

Published by
The National Geographic Society
Melvin M. Payne, *President*
Melville Bell Grosvenor,
    Editor-in-Chief
Frederick G. Vosburgh, *Editor*
Gilbert M. Grosvenor, *Executive
    Editor for this Series*

Prepared by
The Special Publications Division

Robert L. Breeden, *Editor*
Donald J. Crump, *Associate Editor*
Philip B. Silcott, *Manuscript Editor*
Kenneth F. Weaver, *Consulting Editor*
Leon M. Larson, *Assistant to the Editor*
Johanna G. Farren, *Research and Style*
Geraldine Linder, Linda Seeman, Tee
    Loftin Snell, Betty Strauss, *Research*
Richard M. Crum, Ronald M. Fisher,
    William R. Gray, Jr., Gerald S.
    Snyder, *Picture Legends*
Robert Cumming, *Consultant to the
    author on Space Sciences*
Luba Balko, Margaret S. Dean, Carol
    Oakes, Judy Strong, Sandra Turner,
    Barbara Walker, *Editorial Assistants*

Illustrations and Design

Donald J. Crump, *Picture Editor*
Geraldine Linder, Michael E. Long,
    Assistant Picture Editors
Joseph A. Taney, *Art Director*
Josephine B. Bolt, *Assistant
    Art Director*

Production and Printing

Robert W. Messer, *Production*
James R. Whitney, *Engraving and
    Printing*
John R. Metcalfe, *Assistant, Engraving
    and Printing*
Martha Hightower, Virginia
    Thompson, *Index*

*Spewing flame, a thundering Saturn V
rocket disrupts the early morning calm at
Kennedy Space Center, Florida, during its
maiden flight on November 9, 1967. This
mighty rocket will thrust Apollo astronauts
toward the moon. Overleaf: Echo I satellite streaks across the dense, starry center
of the Milky Way Galaxy. Page 1: Carrying their air-conditioners, Astronauts James
A. McDivitt and Edward H. White II walk
toward their Gemini 4 spacecraft on June
3, 1966. Endsheets: A crescent earth hangs
above the moon's horizon in a photograph taken from an altitude of 743 miles
by Lunar Orbiter I on August 23, 1966.*

NATIONAL GEOGRAPHIC PHOTOGRAPHER JOHN E. FLETCH-
ER (RIGHT); HAROLD ABLES, U. S. NAVAL OBSERVATORY,
FLAGSTAFF, ARIZONA (OVERLEAF); N.G.S. PHOTOGRAPHER
OTIS IMBODEN (PAGE ONE); NASA (ENDSHEETS)

FOREWORD

Before boarding *Friendship 7* for lift-off on February 20, 1962, Astronaut John H. Glenn, Jr., carefully tucked a small scrap of blue, brown, and green cloth in with his gear. This piece of material — a miniature National Geographic Society flag — traveled almost five hours in space with the first American to orbit earth. Six months after his flight, the personable Glenn presented the flag to Dr. Melville Bell Grosvenor, the Society's President and Editor, as a salute to the National Geographic's "pioneering contributions to space research" and its "many years of strong support to those men who seek to explore the unknown."

Indeed, your Society has played an integral role in the exploration of space over the past four decades. It has supported many scientists in their endeavors and published their accounts in the NATIONAL GEOGRAPHIC. The Society's interest in space began early with the experiments of such pioneers as Alexander Graham Bell and Robert Goddard; it developed further with such achievements as the ascent of the *Explorer II* balloon 13.71 miles into the stratosphere in 1935 — a flight that held the altitude record for 21 years. Since the advent of the Space Age in 1957, the NATIONAL GEOGRAPHIC has continued to keep its members abreast of the manned and unmanned space ventures that have paved the path leading to the moon. In keeping with this tradition, the Society has prepared *Man's Conquest of Space*, by William R. Shelton, who has written about the space effort since its beginning.

"Before the end of this decade," said the late Dr. Hugh L. Dryden, Director for eleven years of the National Advisory Committee for Aeronautics and a Trustee of the Society, "man will launch his greatest voyage of discovery, a journey whose magnitude and implications for the human race dwarf any high adventure of the past." To meet this challenge to reach the moon — a stepping-stone in the conquest of space — Congress established the National Aeronautics and Space Administration in 1958, and Dr. Dryden became Deputy Administrator. NASA immediately began to coordinate America's immense resources and talents to develop a sound space program. Beginning with the early, exciting days of the first satellites, the Nation's space effort has attained major milestones — successes with the manned Mercury and Gemini flights, and the informative, faithful weather and communications satellites.

After man reaches the moon — what next? Space presents a limitless future and a limitless challenge; the only ingredients needed to surmount them are man's imagination, his desire, and his inventiveness. A quarter of a century ago, few men would have been bold enough to predict seriously that man would reach the moon by 1970. And now, with the impetus already generated and the growing momentum of the space program, who dares prophesy the monumental strides man will take in the coming decades. The world of space holds vast promise for the service of man, and it is a world we have only begun to explore.

JAMES E. WEBB
Administrator, National Aeronautics
and Space Administration

CONTENTS

Setting foot into a new era, an Apollo astronaut descends from his Lunar Module in a planned epochal landing on the bleak, hostile face of the moon.

1/ MAN INVADES SPACE, THE LIMITLESS FRONTIER

For centuries the resolute spirit of the explorer has met every challenge it has encountered—from scorching deserts to frozen expanses of ice, from plunging canyons to defiant mountain peaks, from the ocean depths to the lofty reaches of the atmosphere. But now that man confronts what John F. Kennedy referred to as "this new ocean" of space, he faces the only limitless physical frontier he has ever come up against. Never before has he been able to cut loose the shackles of earth to ascend toward a realm essentially unknown and without boundary.

In August of 1955, before Sputnik I and the dawn of the Space Age, the NATIONAL GEOGRAPHIC called the beckoning ocean of space "the last, the greatest, and the most dangerous frontier of all." How man fares in it may determine not only the nature of his future life on earth but, in a larger sense, whether he has a significant destiny away from his home planet.

As every schoolchild has read—from Novosibirsk in Siberia to Great Falls in Montana—the Russians astonished the world by launching the first artificial satellite on October 4, 1957. On that fateful morning on the grassy steppes of south-central Russia, the countdown inexorably reached *tri . . . dva . . . odin.* Then a great white rocket—in a crescendo of power and sound—climbed into the sky, spun out its cottony contrail, and, as the distant sound funneled out, arched into an elliptical orbit of the earth that would take it 560 miles into space at its highest point.

About 100 minutes after launch, the orbital path of the 184-pound Sputnik brought it again over Russia; excitement mounted at the rocket base. The leader of the Soviet team was a brilliant engineer, Sergei Pavlovich Korolev, a pioneer whom the Russians thought of as "a man who could put rivets in his dreams."

Now, he carefully checked Soviet tracking instruments. In his headset, he could hear a steady "beep beep"—a series of crisp, clear, high-pitched notes that told him Sputnik I was securely in orbit.

FIRST TO ACHIEVE MAN'S DREAM *of space flight, Russian Cosmonaut Yuri Gagarin orbited the earth on April 12, 1961, just 23 days before U. S. Astronaut Alan B. Shepard, Jr., rocketed into space. Major Gagarin, called the Columbus of the Cosmos by his countrymen, died in a plane crash in 1968.*

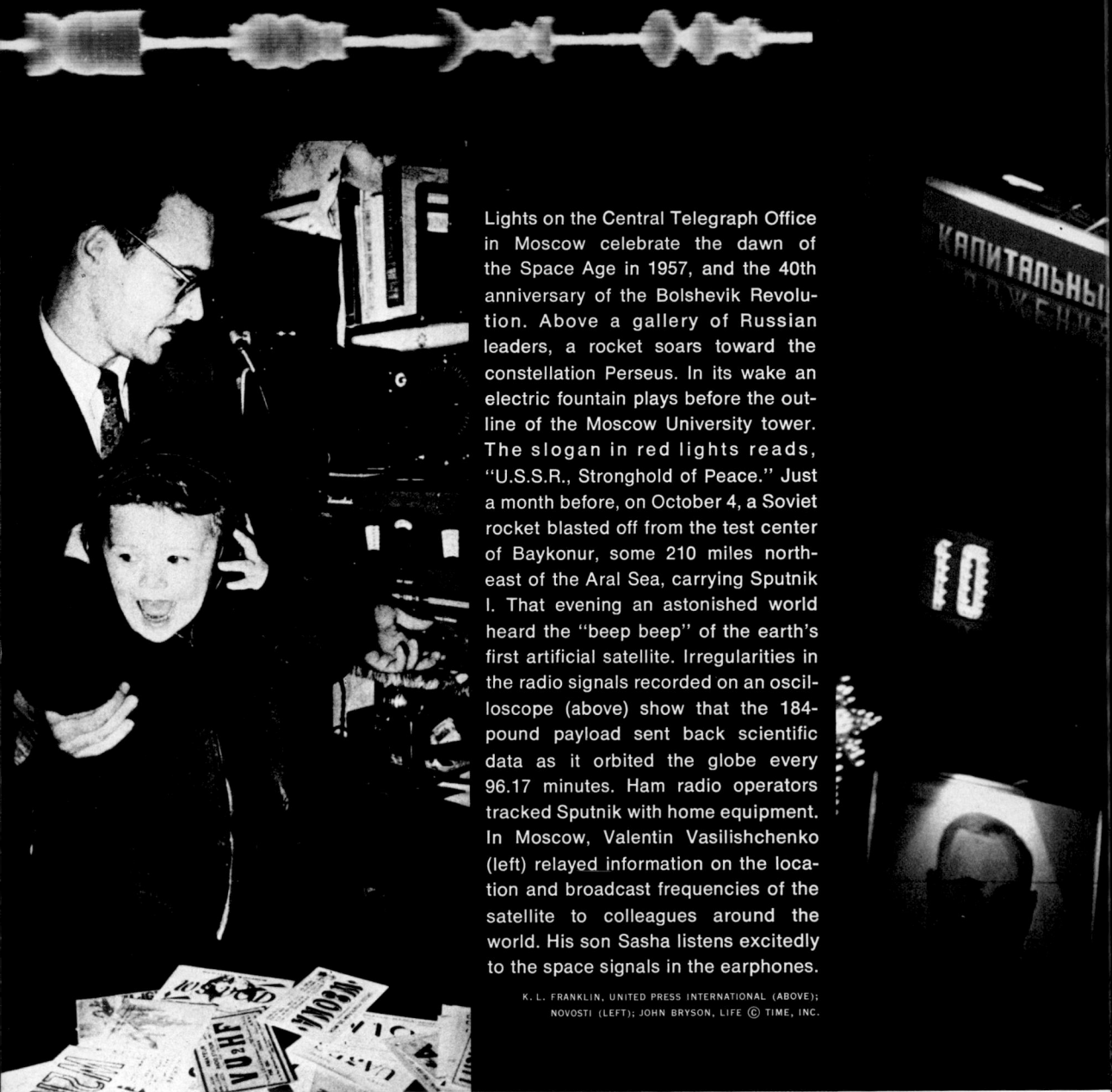

Lights on the Central Telegraph Office in Moscow celebrate the dawn of the Space Age in 1957, and the 40th anniversary of the Bolshevik Revolution. Above a gallery of Russian leaders, a rocket soars toward the constellation Perseus. In its wake an electric fountain plays before the outline of the Moscow University tower. The slogan in red lights reads, "U.S.S.R., Stronghold of Peace." Just a month before, on October 4, a Soviet rocket blasted off from the test center of Baykonur, some 210 miles northeast of the Aral Sea, carrying Sputnik I. That evening an astonished world heard the "beep beep" of the earth's first artificial satellite. Irregularities in the radio signals recorded on an oscilloscope (above) show that the 184-pound payload sent back scientific data as it orbited the globe every 96.17 minutes. Ham radio operators tracked Sputnik with home equipment. In Moscow, Valentin Vasilishchenko (left) relayed information on the location and broadcast frequencies of the satellite to colleagues around the world. His son Sasha listens excitedly to the space signals in the earphones.

K. L. FRANKLIN, UNITED PRESS INTERNATIONAL (ABOVE);
NOVOSTI (LEFT); JOHN BRYSON, LIFE ⓒ TIME, INC.

Later, half a world away, millions more heard the unchallengeable beep of the strange satellite on American radio and television. Amateur astronomers and radio operators around the world confirmed the alien presence.

Commentators struggled to explain the phenomenon: The satellite had arched into space at just such a precise speed and altitude on just such a heading parallel to the surface of the globe that its centrifugal force was in balance with gravity trying to pull it back to earth.

The New York *Times*, struck with the significance of the flight of Sputnik I, said in an editorial: "The creature who descended from a tree or crawled out of a cave a few thousand years ago is now on the eve of incredible journeys."

As the Soviet Union erupted in a mood of exhilaration, the prevailing mood in the United States was one of sober disappointment that our own Vanguard satellite, then awaiting launch at Cape Canaveral, Florida, had not led the way into space. President Dwight D. Eisenhower had announced that the United States, as part of the International Geophysical Year of 1957-58, would attempt to orbit a satellite, but Russia had been first.

We had scarcely adjusted to the implications of Sputnik I when a second shoe fell. Just 30 days later, on November 3, 1957, the Soviet Union

launched not simply an instrumented sphere, but a 1,120-pound payload. Sputnik II contained, besides a store of scientific instruments, a small black-and-white dog named Laika.

American scientists realized at once that the Russian mastery of the art of rocketry was indeed formidable. And they knew that the achievement of supporting life in the alternating bake-freeze of space was a highly delicate and complex undertaking. Aside from the sophisticated life-support system the Soviets used, other instrumentation on board was designed to investigate the ionosphere, cosmic rays and other radiation, and the nature of the earth's electromagnetic field.

About a week after launch, signals from Laika's sensors stopped, indicating she had died. But the half-ton Sputnik II satellite and its rocket still remained in orbit three weeks later when those of us interested in seeing the long-awaited Vanguard launch assembled at Cape Canaveral.

The scene leading up to lift-off — T-minus-0 — was as charged with drama as those days, hours, and minutes that toll off the approach of battle. The launch was a highly public affair; "Research in a fishbowl," one reporter called it. Each day headlines shouted across the land that the countdown was on, then off, then on and off again, as delays mounted.

I recall one night when I strolled down the beach across the Port Canaveral inlet from Pad 18-A. The red and white lights on the Vanguard gantry danced in the dark waters. In the reflection, the Vanguard rocket was transformed from a solidly poised stalagmite aimed at the heavens to a wavering stalactite pointing to the depths of the sea—a visual paradox that somehow matched my mood alternating between hope and concern.

This was a December night, and even in Florida the beach felt cold and damp from the surf. Newsmen, sipping hot coffee, huddled near a line of driftwood fires blazing along the fringe of rustling palmettos and sea grapes. Missile buffs, or "bird watchers," mingled with them, occasionally joining in song.

Flickering lances of firelight outlined the hulks of trucks and moving vans that photographers had positioned on the beach as bases for their cameras. Shoreward, sea oats swayed in the wind, and in the dunes the light played on an incongruous battery of the tripods and telephoto lenses of the press—pointing toward Vanguard like the remorseless snouts of cannon.

The final countdown began at 1 a.m. on December 6. We heard little singing that night as we waited out a lead-colored dawn. Then through binoculars we saw a rime of frost building up on Vanguard's first stage as the subzero LOX (liquid oxygen) was pumped aboard. At 11:44 a.m. the rocket's umbilical, or service, cords dropped away. Launch was imminent. I strained for a clearer view of a moment of history.

Suddenly a splayed tongue of flame darted from the base of the rocket. Was this the fire of ignition —or something else? Vanguard began to rise. Then it stopped. It began to sink back. As it fell into its own launch ring, its thin skin ruptured. Instantly, a mass of incandescent red flame and boiling black smoke engulfed the rocket. The exploding fireball blossomed 70 feet high as LOX and kerosene combined in a fiery demise.

In a few seconds it was all over—a national aspiration gone up in flame and smoke. The intended satellite, which Soviet Premier Nikita S. Khrushchev was later to call an "orange," broadcast its cry not from the lofty throne of space as had been planned but from the palmetto flats where grew thistle, swamp myrtle, and thyme.

As the news spread to a waiting Nation and world, it became obvious that the United States—

FIERY EXPLOSION *consumes America's Vanguard rocket—and abruptly ends the country's first attempt to orbit a satellite. Vanguard's nose cone topples seconds after the blast on December 6, 1957, at Cape Canaveral. Above, technicians preparing for the launch effort position the nose cone above the rocket's 3.25-pound payload. Less than two months later, on January 31, Explorer I rode a flame-tipped rocket into an elliptical orbit, reaching 1,573 miles at its highest point, and blazed the trail for America's entry into the age of space.*

on the surface at least—had suffered a catastrophe of enormous magnitude.

"Overnight," Dr. Wernher von Braun later summarized, "it became popular to question the bulwarks of our society, our public education system, our industrial strength, international policy, defense strategy and forces, the capability of our science and technology. Even the moral fiber of our people came under searching examination."

Many scientists warned that so great was the difference between the 1,120-pound Sputnik II with its life-supporting atmosphere and the tiny 3.25-pound Vanguard satellite, that it would be years before the United States could catch up.

MAXWELL COPLAN, DESIGN PHOTOGRAPHERS INTERNATIONAL (ABOVE) AND U. S. ARMY

JUPITER-C ROCKET *towers above Army technicians (opposite) as the countdown begins for Explorer I on January 31, 1958. Evaporating liquid oxygen swirls around the feet of the men (below) as they fuel the rocket at Cape Canaveral—renamed Cape Kennedy in 1963. At a blackboard, rocket expert Dr. Wernher von Braun, then Director, Development Operations Division of the Army Ballistic Missile Agency at Huntsville, Alabama, traces the satellite's trajectory after launching.*

Pentagon officers pointed to a similar disparity in the relative sizes of booster rockets, which doubled as intercontinental ballistic missiles.

Against this background of pessimism in the days following Sputnik II, the United States pressed into service a unique team of rocket specialists. Dr. von Braun and his group of about a hundred former German rocketmen, then civilians working for the U. S. Army at Huntsville, Alabama, were instructed to prepare for the launching of an artificial satellite. Thus began one of the most brilliant chapters in the American conquest of space. Ever since the German rocketmen had been transported to the United States to live, von Braun and his specialists had proposed orbiting a satellite. Now, with the world watching, they had their chance.

On November 8, 1957, when von Braun and U. S. Army Maj. Gen. John B. Medaris at last got the green light, von Braun promised to put a satellite into orbit within 90 days.

On the night of January 31, many of us who had seen the exploding Vanguard's crimson glow stain the blockhouse walls assembled again at Cape Canaveral—this time to see if Explorer I could succeed where Vanguard had not. Officials allowed us inside the Cape to a press site about a mile from the launch pad. When I first saw the

Jupiter-C booster, it already radiated incredible luster inside its ring of searchlights. Through binoculars, its ice-encrusted form glistened like a pillar of cavern quartz caught in glaring light. The crisscrossing beams went on to pierce the blackness of the night sky above the rocket, as if pointing out the path to the stars. The entire Cape, with its ghostly array of antennas, theodolites, and towers, was in an eerie state of suspension. Photographers nervously checked their cameras every few minutes.

Just before 10 p.m. a foggy-throated warning horn sounded mournfully across the palmetto flats. At 10:38 the 18.13-pound satellite and the rocket's

SCANNING THE SKY *above New Mexico, a Smithsonian Institution Baker-Nunn tracking camera pinpoints Explorer I. Jubilant scientists — Dr. William H. Pickering, Director of the Jet Propulsion Laboratory at Pasadena, California, Dr. James A. Van Allen, and Dr. von Braun — hoist a mock-up of the final stage and payload. In the 112 days its batteries operated, the satellite transmitted cosmic ray, micrometeorite, and temperature data, and revealed a radiation belt later named for Van Allen.*

upper stages started slowly to whirl, then rapidly wound up until the tip of the rocket was spinning at nearly 500 revolutions per minute, providing stability for the payload during flight.

The final tolling of the countdown seemed

irrevocable. Suddenly, the bluish-white rocket spurted fire. A pink cloud of smoke and steam blossomed instantly. The rocket rose, gained speed, roaring out its power in great surges of sound that drowned out the muffled fragments of cheers. The rising flame-tipped stiletto pierced a cloud; then its light — redder now — reappeared above the clouds, coursing higher.

The launch was sheer majesty. Explorer I was on its way. A friend of mine, CBS newscaster Charles Von Fremd, approached, his face and clothes wet with perspiration.

"That's the greatest thrill I've ever had in reporting," Chuck breathlessly exclaimed. "I felt patriotic all of a sudden, watching that lovely little son-of-a-gun go up there!"

As Explorer I went into orbit, well within von Braun's three-month estimate, the Nation fully shared our jubilation and pride; the United States had staked out a claim. Explorer I was followed by the successful launch of Vanguard I on March 17, 1958. Now we, like the Russians, had dispatched two representatives to emerge beyond our lower atmosphere.

Explorer I, during its 1,573-mile reach into space at the height of its elliptical orbit, revealed an earth-girdling band of trapped solar radiation. The band, a potential hazard to astronauts, became

N.G.S. PHOTOGRAPHER DEAN CONGER (ABOVE) AND BILL TAUB, NASA

STRIDING PURPOSEFULLY *across Cape Canaveral's Pad 5, from transfer van to Redstone rocket, Mercury Astronaut Alan B. Shepard, Jr., keeps a rendezvous with history on May 5, 1961. He carries an air conditioner to cool his pressure suit, and wears plastic overshoes to avoid tracking dirt into the space capsule. The suborbital flight, first U. S. manned mission, carried Shepard 302 miles to splashdown in the Atlantic. In an earlier simulated shot, Shepard (left) tests his equipment.*

The over-all space mission was broadly based and incorporated many aspects of exploration, from meteorology to communications, but its later directive to send a man into space was most eagerly embraced by the public. The first phase of the manned-flight effort was Project Mercury, a program to construct a vehicle to carry one astronaut. First, we would aim him like an artillery shell on a ballistic trajectory to carry him briefly into space. Then we would try something infinitely more difficult: We would attempt to send an astronaut into earth orbit.

NASA selected and began to train its first class of astronauts, undertook a massive construction program, and initiated a worldwide network of tracking stations for both unmanned and manned satellites. As the months passed, Project Mercury moved steadily toward its appointment with whatever destiny awaited the first man to venture into space. There were rumors that Russia, too, was preparing to send men into orbit. The question often arose: Who would blaze the trail, the United States or the U.S.S.R.?

Wherever I traveled during the first few months of 1961—at Langley Field, Virginia, home of the NASA Space Task Group, at the spacecraft factory of McDonnell Aircraft Corporation in St. Louis, at Cape Canaveral itself—I heard nothing but confidence that America would lead the way. In February the country learned the names of the men chosen for special training for the debut in space —Navy Lt. Comdr. Alan B. Shepard, Jr., Marine Lt. Col. John H. Glenn, Jr., and Air Force Capt. Virgil I. Grissom. Triumph seemed assured.

But the honor of orbiting the first man was not to be ours. I was having breakfast in Chicago on April 12 when I received word that Russia had sent Maj. Yuri Alekseyevich Gagarin around the earth. To reach the Cape as quickly as possible, I took a jet to Tampa, Florida, then went by rental car across the peninsula to the Atlantic.

known as the Van Allen belt, after Dr. James A. Van Allen, designer of the satellite's instrumentation. A later probe indicated a second similar belt. Vanguard I, through deviations in its orbital path, confirmed earlier beliefs that the earth is almost imperceptibly pear-shaped.

Our emotional, scientific, military, and economic commitment to space had become a fact. Congress and public alike called for a more ambitious program. On President Eisenhower's recommendation, Congress created a single federal space agency, the National Aeronautics and Space Administration. The agency, built on the nucleus of the old National Advisory Committee for Aeronautics, began operation in October, 1958.

NASA eventually acquired, in addition to thousands of scientists and technicians, many military and quasi-military organizations, facilities, and equipment. The Army was directed to transfer to the agency not only von Braun and his 4,200-member group at Huntsville but also more than $100 million worth of facilities required to design, develop, test, build, and launch space vehicles. Not least of the rich legacy inherited by NASA were the detailed plans for the Saturn I, the first rocket especially designed by the U. S. for space flight.

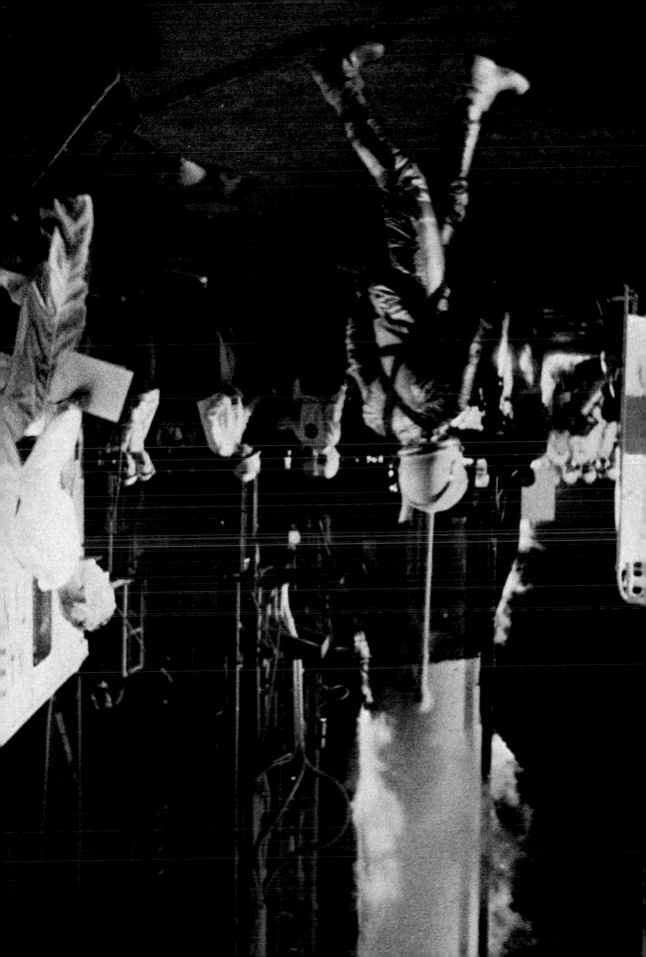

CHEERS of spectators on Cocoa Beach (left) rise with Shepard as the Redstone rocket lifts off at the Cape. The 83-foot, 33-ton "bird," photographed through a 600-millimeter lens, appears closer than its actual distance of six miles. After the mission, Shepard, joined by the other six Mercury astronauts, received NASA's Distinguished Service Medal from President John F. Kennedy at the White House. The President inadvertently dropped the medal, quipped, "This decoration has gone from the ground up," and joined in the spacemen's laughter.

SWINGING ABOVE HIS CAPSULE, Astronaut Shepard peers upward at the Marine helicopter plucking him from the sea. "Good boy!" he later told the pilot. The chopper carried him and the capsule, Freedom 7, to the aircraft carrier Lake Champlain for preliminary medical and technical debriefing.

An hour after I reached my motel, where press cables were already being strung out for the impending Shepard flight, I had dinner with two of our astronauts, Donald ("Deke") Slayton and Gordon ("Gordo") Cooper, and two of their physicians, Dr. William K. Douglas and Dr. Carmault B. Jackson, Jr. As we ate roast beef in Cocoa Beach's Ramon's restaurant and discussed the space program, we all agreed on one thing: We were deeply disappointed that the first man had not been an American. But as we got up to leave, Deke added a note of optimism.

"There's one good thing about Gagarin's flight," he said. "It proves there is no serious obstacle to a man going into space. Maybe we ought to be happy to know that it can be done."

Twenty-three days later, the press again entered the launch complex of Cape Canaveral, this time shortly before dawn, to witness what we hoped would be one of the great milestones of the decade. Clouds obscured half the sky, and as the sun rose above a gray bank of scud over the Atlantic, it tinted undulating wraiths of ground fog an incredible rosy gold. By 9:30 a.m. the countdown for Freedom 7 had just four minutes to go. Nerves were taut.

"Well," said my friend Chuck Von Fremd nervously, "Alan is on his own now."

21

"Four . . . three . . . two . . . one . . . zero . . . Ignition . . . Lift-off!"

Alan Shepard's calm, unhurried radio voice came to us. "This is 7 . . . Fuel is go . . . and the oxygen is go. . . . Cabin pressure is holding at five point five."

The rising rocket plunged into a cloud, its flame appearing to perish like a match smothered in moisture. But the rocket reappeared, thrusting upward, gaining altitude. I vaguely heard cheers and applause.

"What a beautiful view!" Alan exclaimed as he reached maximum altitude of 116.5 miles. The shot was going to be successful.

America's pioneer astronaut and his Mercury capsule performed flawlessly, and he later shared credit with the thousands of scientists, engineers, and technicians directly involved in the 15-minute, 302-mile suborbital flight.

Slightly over two months later, millions watched on television as "Gus" Grissom repeated Shepard's success — except for the accidental sinking of his capsule, *Liberty Bell 7,* after completion of the mission. Then in February of 1962, millions more were engrossed with the drama of John Glenn's three orbits of the earth in *Friendship 7.* When the smiling Marine Colonel made his sincerity and sense of humor evident in Washington, in New York, and in other cities, Americans everywhere had a new light in their eyes and a new lift in their hearts.

"In the saddle of success," wrote Saul Pett of the Associated Press, "he rode loose and easy, and everyone found something to like."

So absorbing was this initial phase as man himself penetrated the cosmos that we scarcely realized how many records had fallen almost overnight. Before rockets carried man into space, a number of painstakingly prepared ventures had attempted to send him to ever greater altitudes and speeds. In 1935 the U. S. Army Air Corps and the National Geographic Society sent balloonists Capt. Albert W. Stevens and Capt. Orvil A. Anderson to a record altitude of 13.71 miles.

On May 4, 1961, the day before Alan Shepard's flight, the Navy sent Comdr. Malcolm D. Ross and Lt. Comdr. Victor A. Prather, Jr., in the Strato-Lab balloon to a record of 21.5 miles. The X-15 rocket plane and other experimental aircraft had often taken man to great heights, but the record altitude before the beginning of manned space flight was the 25.85 miles reached by X-15 pilot Robert M. White on August 12, 1960.

Suddenly — befitting a major and compelling technological breakthrough — all records were left far behind. The orbital speed of Yuri Gagarin and John Glenn was around 17,500 miles per hour — enough to circle the planet at their altitude in about 90 minutes. This compared with the record of 2,196 miles per hour previously reached by Joseph A. Walker in the X-15 on August 4, 1960. During orbital flight both Gagarin and Glenn soared above 160 miles. The advent of space flight now meant that man had to create a new time scale and drastically readjust his earthly concept of speed and distance.

With the personification of space conquest in the form of dedicated astronauts, and with the inauguration of manned flights, our national and personal involvement in our final frontier reached a new high. On May 25, 1961, President Kennedy underscored our commitment to space and made our objective precise and bold when he stated that the United States should achieve the goal, "before this decade is out, of landing a man on the moon and returning him safely to the earth. No single space project in this period will be more impressive to mankind, or more important for the long-range exploration of space. . . ." Our ultimate destiny beyond this planet remains unknown, but after this announcement the means by which we could leave the earth were solidly forged.

Most of us know what followed the establishment of our target in the sky. Twenty thousand corporations, 300,000 people, ten major NASA centers, and well over $23 billion eventually were dedicated to the task. Step by step — through space walks and spacecraft maneuvers — people saw progress toward the moon.

Simultaneously, space began to open up treasures in manifold areas. Instrumented probes uncovered fascinating secrets about the moon, Mars,

FIRST AMERICAN TO ORBIT *the earth, Lt. Col. John H. Glenn, Jr., flashes battery-powered fingertip lights in a preflight test at Cape Canaveral. He used them during times of darkness on his 83,450-mile journey of February 20, 1962. Soon after the mission, Vice President Lyndon B. Johnson, on behalf of the National Geographic Society, presented the astronaut with the Hubbard Medal, the Society's highest honor in the field of research and exploration.*

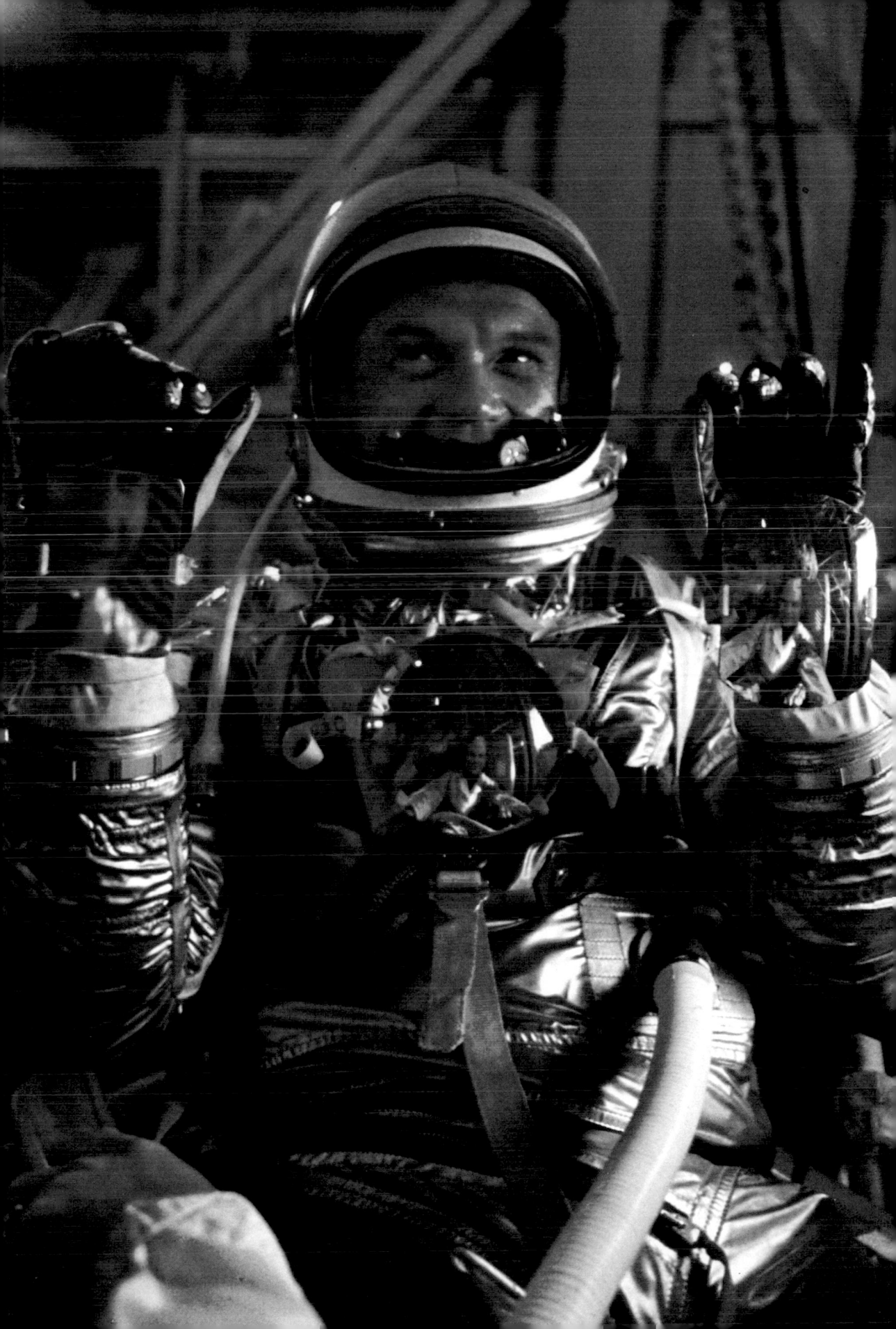

"SPIN-OFF" BENEFIT *of the space program, a monitor checks pulse and respiration of a subject at General Dynamics, San Diego, California. Developed for use on astronauts, it works without electrodes attached to the skin, promising special help for badly burned patients. An instrument adapted from a micrometeorite impact sensor (below) records the heartbeat of a chicken embryo at NASA's Ames Research Center, Moffett Field, California; with it, doctors hope to detect tremors of Parkinson's disease.*

SNUG AGAINST THE CHILL, *a camper curls up in a blanket made of material derived from insulation used to protect booster-rocket instruments from extreme temperatures. Another blanket reflects heat from the campfire. Warmer than wool, waterproof, windproof, washable, and*

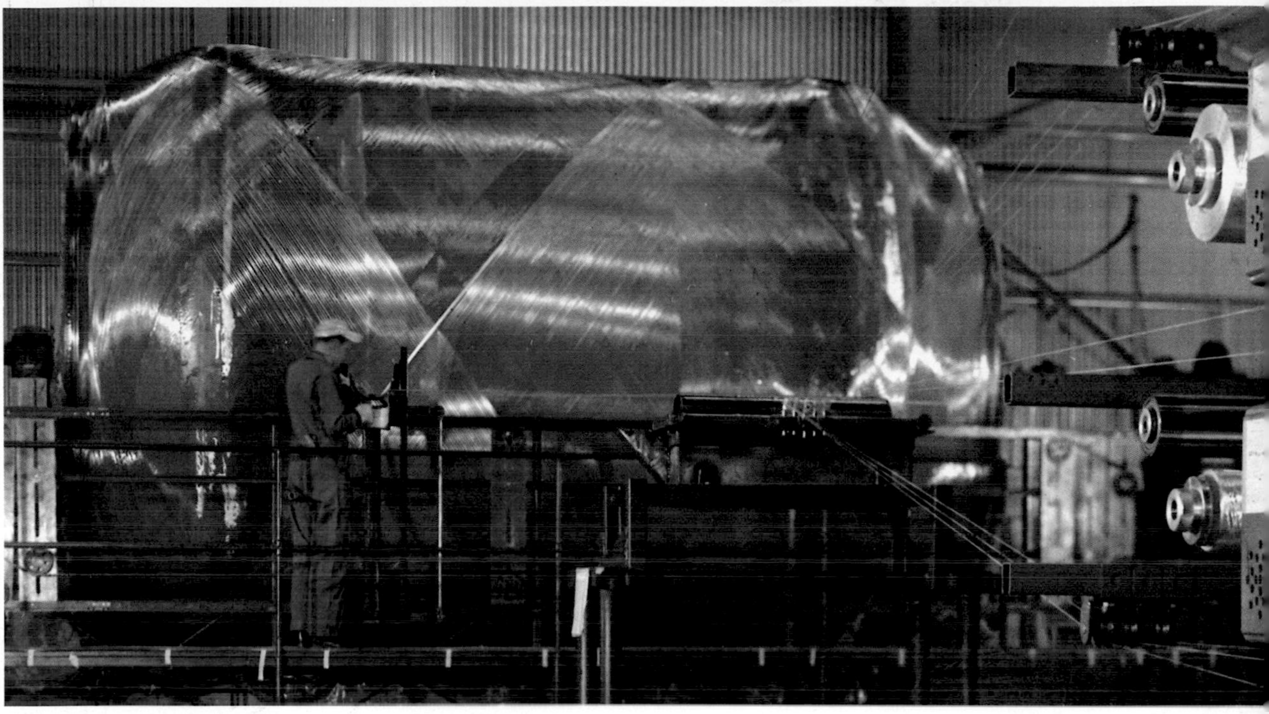

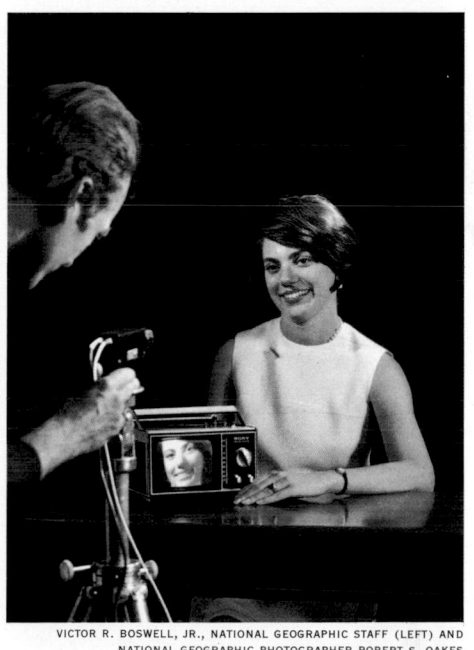

ROCKET-ENGINE CASINGS *grow from millions of feet of glass fiber spun around a removable core, then impregnated with resin and finally baked for hardness at the United Technology Center in Sunnyvale, California. A similar process produces reinforced plastic mortar pipe, like the length of water main (left) being buried near Grass Valley, California. The tube weighs one-sixth as much as reinforced concrete pipe and resists corrosion and deterioration. Strong and resilient, it will bounce even if dropped on a hard surface.*

weighing only 12 ounces, the covering traps some 80 percent of the user's body heat. Duck hunters and ice fishermen find it especially useful.

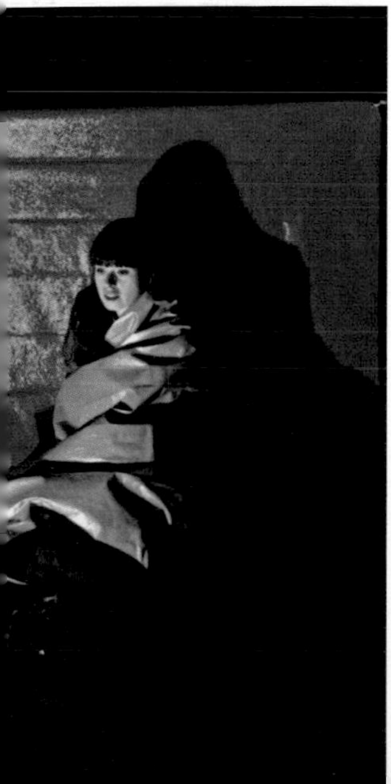

SILICON CHIP *housing 44 electronic components passes through the eye of a needle. Such miniature circuitry, developed for Minuteman computers, makes possible a TV camera barely larger than a cigarette pack. Its uses include underwater research and mobile news coverage.*

VICTOR R. BOSWELL, JR., NATIONAL GEOGRAPHIC STAFF (LEFT) AND NATIONAL GEOGRAPHIC PHOTOGRAPHER ROBERT S. OAKES

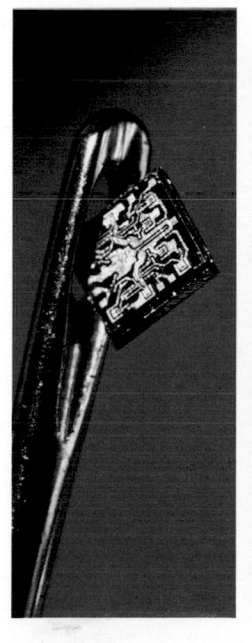

Venus, and the sun. We watched events, via television relay satellites, as they occurred in Europe, Asia, Africa, and South America. We spotted hurricanes with meteorological satellites and established the World Meteorological Center at Suitland, Maryland. Transatlantic jet pilots now routinely pick up the latest satellite photographs of their routes. In addition, commercial communications satellites relay telephone conversations and teletype messages instantly across the oceans. Scientists using rocket astronomy have discovered more than 20 celestial bodies within our own galaxy that emit mysterious X-rays.

In medicine we have gleaned a host of benefits. Remote sensing devices used to monitor pulse, respiration, and other body functions of astronauts have found their way into hospitals. A remarkable array of prosthetic and diagnostic devices has resulted, including probes that take pictures inside the human body.

Satellite observations of the earth's surface have provided unexpected dividends to geologists, oceanographers, mineralogists, and foresters. Benefits to industry and the consumer can already be measured. Industry has found uses for corrosion-resistant alloys, even plastic railway tank cars derived from rocket-propellant tanks. Consumers can count a variety of items—from heat-resistant smoking-pipe liners to more efficient farm tractors.

By the end of the first decade of the Space Age, the new science of astronautics had embraced virtually every scientific field—from astrophysics to zoology. And it was apparent that the United States had committed itself as firmly to space as it had earlier committed itself to aviation. The mystique of space had secured a grip on the consciousness of man, and the lure of the cosmos would tempt him ever farther from the accustomed gravity of his birthplace.

"The earth is the cradle of humanity," wrote the Russian father of rocketry, Konstantin Tsiolkovsky, "but mankind will not stay in the cradle forever."

HALF PLANE, HALF ROCKET SHIP, *the X-15 drops from the wing of its parent B-52 some 45,000 feet above Nevada. The research craft will plummet like a bomb for 1,450 feet, then its 600,000-horsepower engine will ignite and boost it to the edge of space. The X-15 has soared to 67 miles—higher than any other winged aircraft—and traveled at 4,534 mph, twice the speed of a high-power rifle bullet.*

NATIONAL GEOGRAPHIC PHOTOGRAPHER DEAN CONGER, NASA

2/ SCIENCE AND FANTASY, A CHRONICLE OF SPACE

One clear night not long ago I was picnicking with friends on a beach beside the Gulf of Mexico. Suddenly, one of them pointed upward. "There's a satellite!" he yelled. A few seconds later his wife also pointed. "I see it," she exclaimed. "It looks just like a moving star!"

The rest of us were momentarily confused because each was pointing in a different direction, but we quickly realized that not one but two artificial satellites were clearly visible overhead. Twenty minutes later we spotted a third pinpoint of light tracing its silent path across the dark sky.

These visible and conspicuous symbols of the Space Age still fill me with a sense of awe and mystery. Ancient man must have been no less awed by the lights he saw in the night sky. For him, the moon dominated the starry heavens, rising and setting and regularly changing its shape. At long intervals he beheld the intrusion of alien lights with long tapering tails. And he noticed numerous fiery streaks, ranging from the apparent size of embers to great bolts of light that exploded in soundless incandescence. From time to time the skies glowed with strange lucent clouds, pulsed with eerie shrouds and wraiths, or appeared to come alive with mysterious luminosities.

Of all objects in space, the daytime star, the sun, played the dominant legendary role. To the Egyptians, the sun was a god who had to be appeased by offerings from earth. The ancient Chinese believed a shaggy dwarf named P'an Ku created the sun—as well as the rest of the universe—with hammer and chisel.

In a more practical sense, ancient man used the sun to tell the time of day, and the time of a year composed of 365 sunrises. As early as 3000 B.C., the Egyptians and the Sumerians had devised and refined calendars. With the calendars, certain learned people, sometimes referred to as the natural astrologers, often predicted accurately the movements of heavenly bodies. This rudimentary ability to project human intelligence into the

(Continued on page 35)

EARTH'S AWESOME STAR, *an object of mystery and worship through the ages, bestows warmth and beauty upon mankind. Here the great yellow disk sets the horizon ablaze at Big Bend National Park in southern Texas, and spins an arc of light off the mirror of the photographer's reflex-camera lens.*

CAIRO MUSEUM, AUDRAIN-SAMIVEL

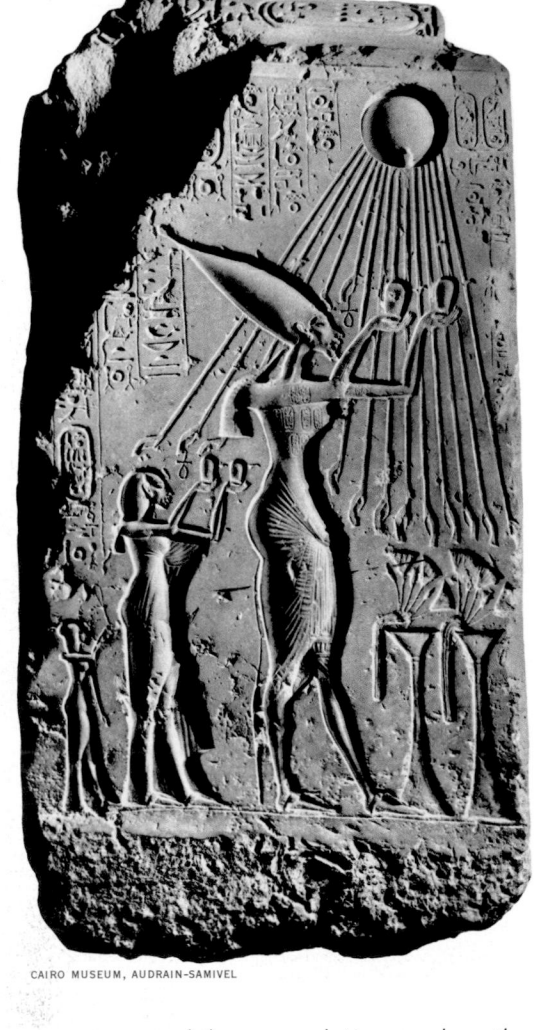

HAND-TIPPED RAYS *of the sun god Aten reach earthward to scatter the gift of life. In hollow relief, Egypt's Pharaoh Akhenaten and Queen Nefertiti present offerings at a religious ceremony of the 14th century B.C. Condemning lesser deities, the king proclaimed one god only—Aten. Worshipers built luxurious temples and exalted the sun in hymns.*

MYTHICAL SPACE TRAVELER, *Icarus plunges to his death in the Aegean Sea after his wings of feathers and wax melted when he flew too close to the sun. His father Daedalus, who fashioned the wings, watches helplessly. Sketched in oil by the 17th-century Flemish painter Peter Paul Rubens, the Greek myth reflects man's ages-old longing to travel into space.*

ROYAL MUSEUM, BELGIUM

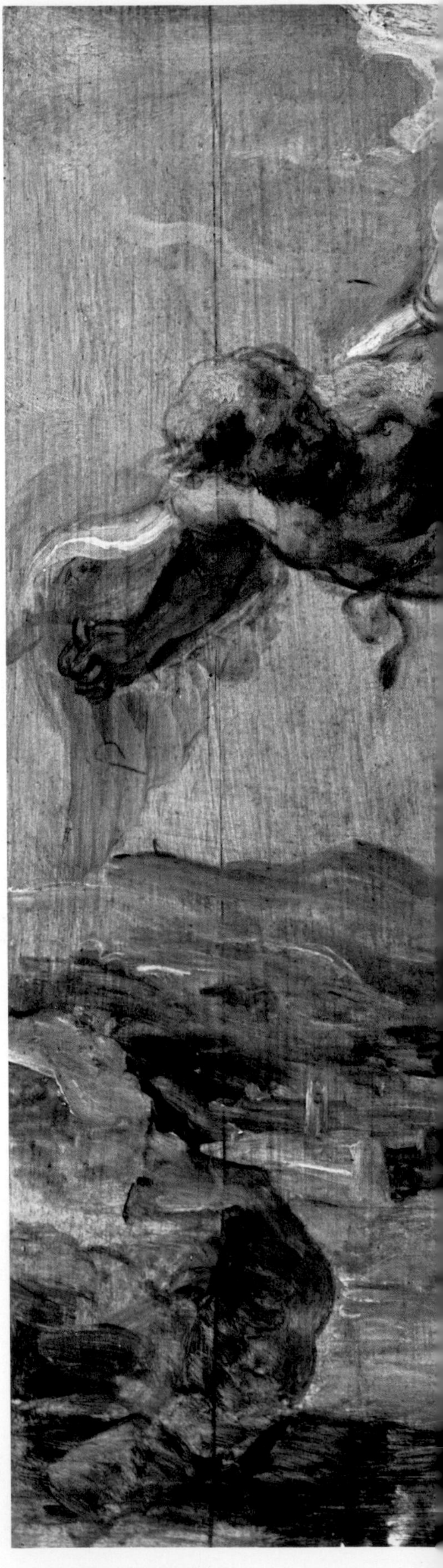

DETAIL OF PAINTING BY GIOVANNI DI PAOLO, COURTESY LEHMAN COLLECTION

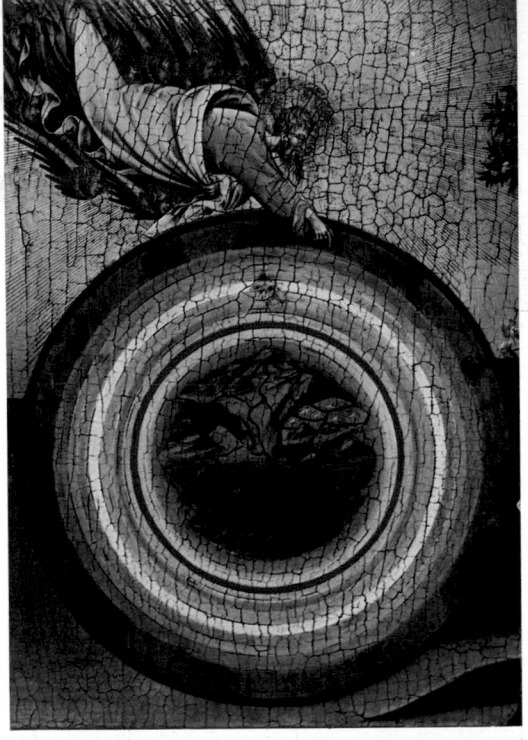

EARTH-CENTERED UNIVERSE: *Paths of the planets appear as colored bands circling a fancied world in this detail of a 15th-century panel "Expulsion of Adam and Eve From Paradise." Set forth by the astronomer Ptolemy in the second century, this concept prevailed for more than a thousand years.*

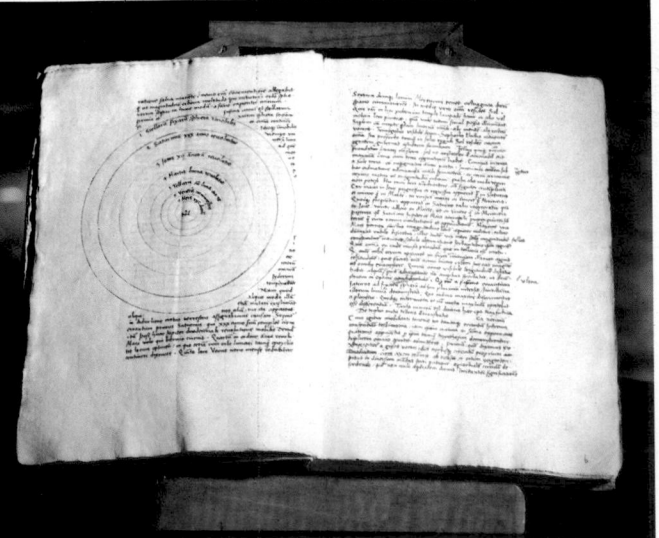

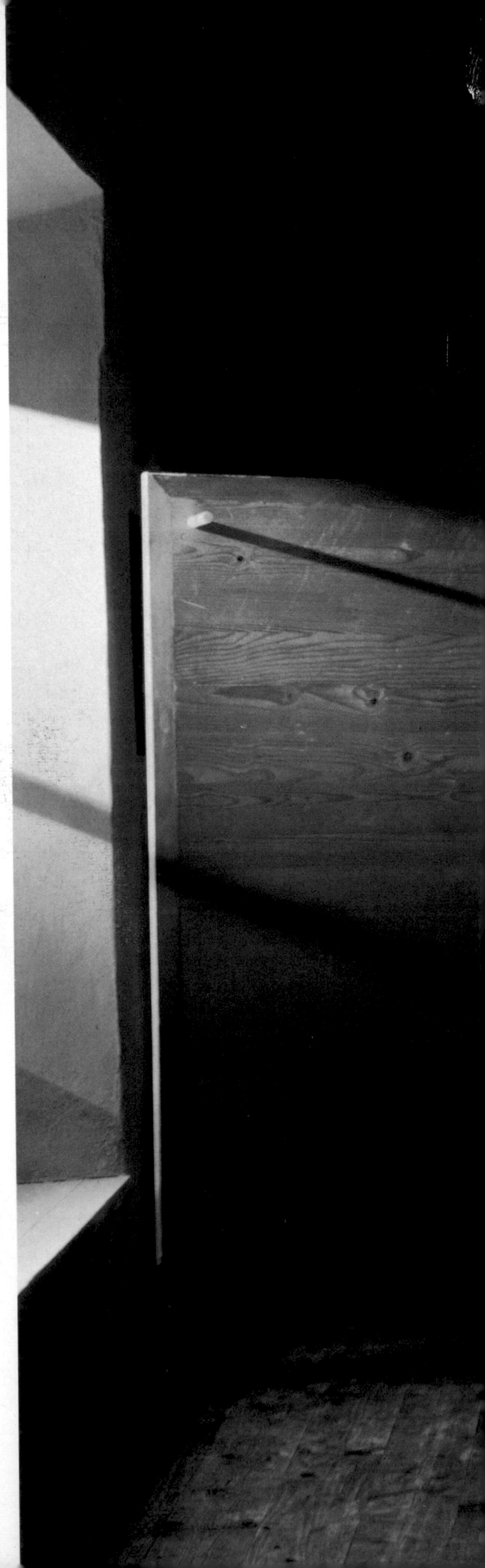

WOODEN QUADRANT *still gauges the sun's angle at Frombork, Poland, in the study of Nicolaus Copernicus, 15th-century astronomer who formulated a new theory of the universe, placing the sun at the center of the solar system. His treatise, at Krakow's Jagiellonian University, shows his concept of the orbits of the planets known in his day.*

ERICH LESSING, MAGNUM

FIRST SCIENTIST *to turn the telescope upon the heavens, Galileo Galilei began a systematic study of the night sky in 1609. The instrument (below, right) points toward the Doge's Palace from a balcony of St. Mark's Cathedral in Venice, Italy. The city's amazed Doge, Leonardo Dona, looked through Galileo's telescope at islands and ships in the Gulf of Venice. Before a window framing the leaning tower of Pisa rest two experimental spheres. Legend says that Galileo, intrigued by how objects moved, dropped two such different-sized stone balls from the tower and watched as they struck the ground almost simultaneously, thus disproving the ancient theory that a large body would fall twice as fast as one half its weight.*

PAINTING BY GIUSTO SUSTERMAN, UFFIZI GALLERY, SCALA

ERICH LESSING, MAGNUM

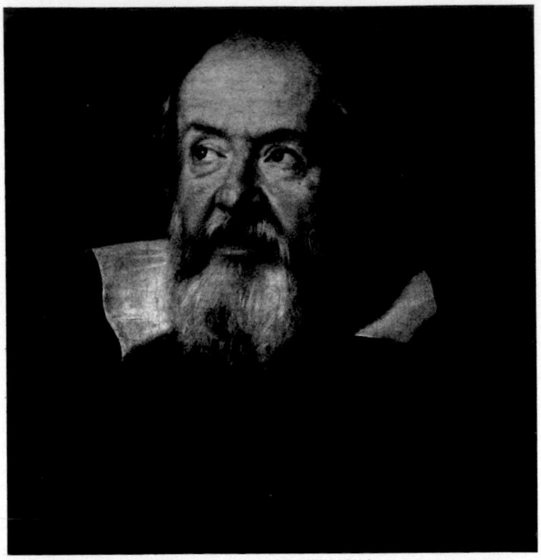

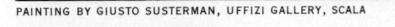

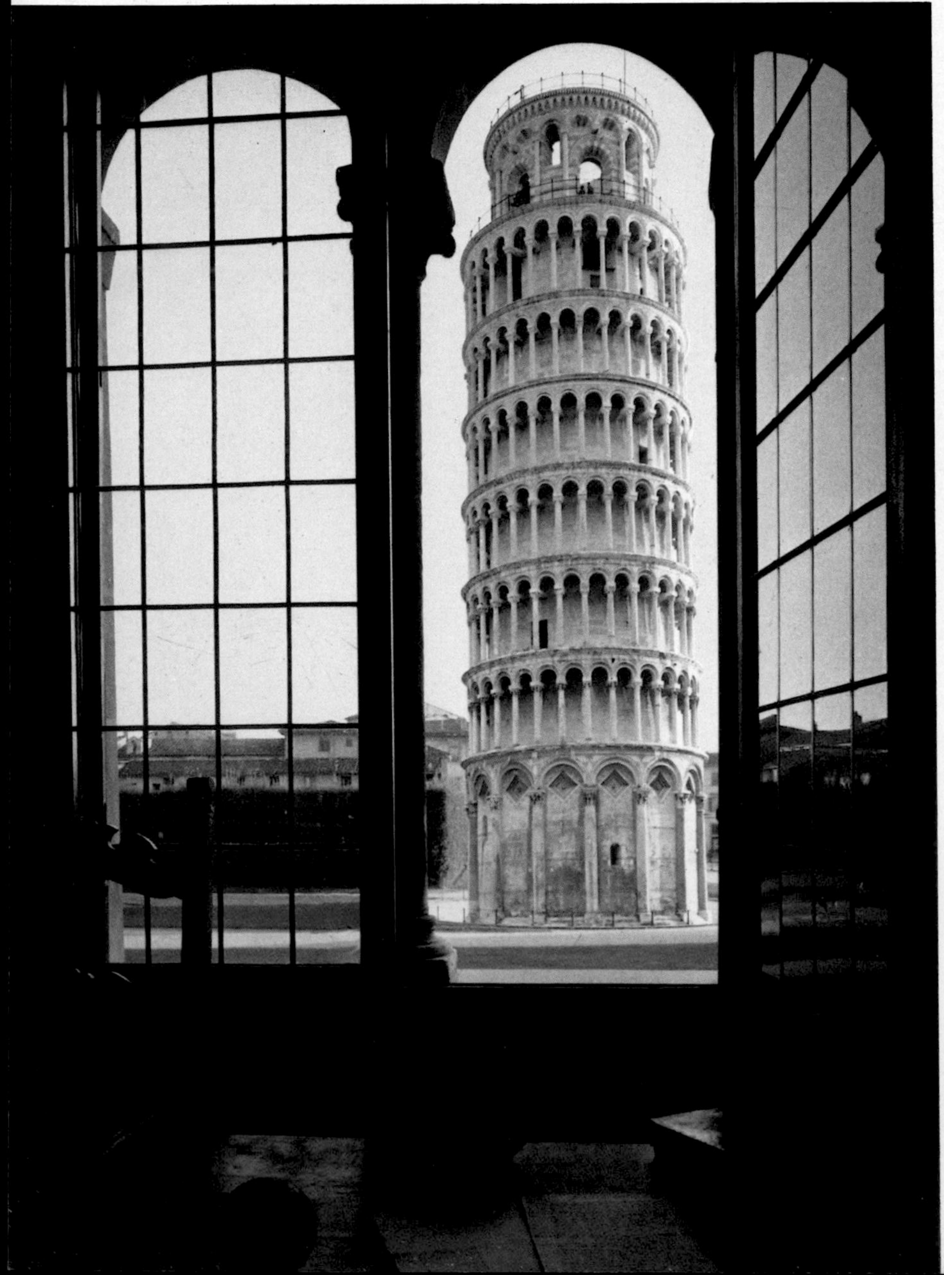

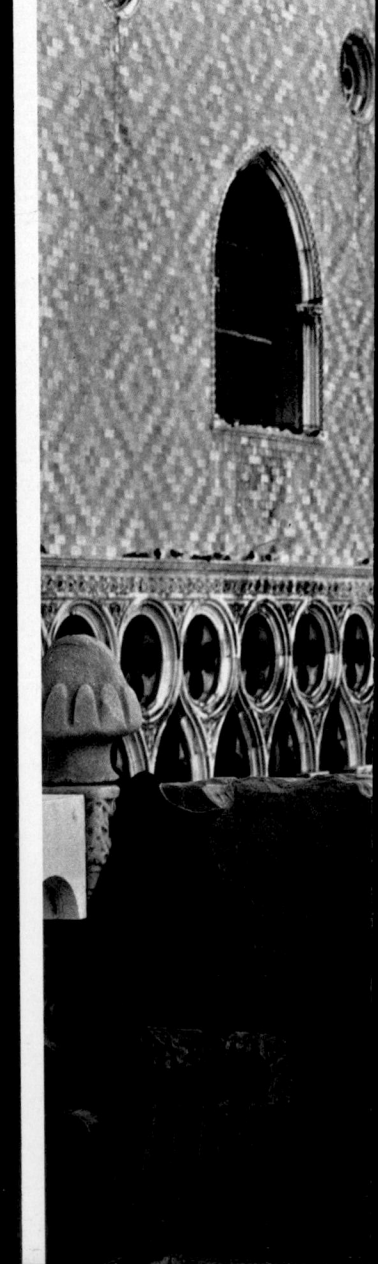

future encouraged another group, the judicial astrologers, to maintain that celestial objects could influence historical and natural events on earth. Thus, early study of the universe led to the belief that the fates of individuals and the advent of wars, floods, and plagues could be predicted by the relative position of heavenly bodies.

When the Greek astronomer Aristarchus first advanced the possibility — 22 centuries ago — that the heavens did not revolve around the earth, few paid him any attention. Man preferred to believe that the earth was unique in the universe, and all else existed to serve it.

In the 2d century A.D. a Greek astronomer named Claudius Ptolemy, who lived in Egypt, published an encyclopedia of all man's beliefs concerning the universe. Now known by its Arab name, *Almagest*, Ptolemy's treatise accepted the view of another Greek, Hipparchus, that an immovable earth was at the center of the universe and that around it orbited the moon, the sun, and the planets. Ptolemy remained the supreme authority for more than a thousand years.

In 1543 the great Polish astronomer Nicolaus Copernicus published his theory that the planets revolved in perfect circles around the sun. Later, the brilliant German astronomer Johannes Kepler formulated new laws of planetary motion. Kepler's

ENGLISH SCIENTIST *Isaac Newton, born in 1642, the year Galileo died, used precise mathematical equations to refine the Italian's theories. Whereas Galileo discovered how objects moved, Newton discovered why, explaining almost every motion in the universe with his Law of Universal Gravitation. On the windowsill of Newton's study at Woolsthorpe Manor stands a replica of his reflecting telescope. The instrument reflects light from a magnifying curved mirror near the base to a flat mirror near the eyepiece at the top. The desk holds a copy of Newton's* Mathematical Principles of Natural Philosophy, *his 1687 lexicon of mechanics, foundation of astronomy and physics.*

principal conclusion was that the planets orbit the sun not in perfect circles but in ellipses.

The telescope, as utilized by the Italian Galileo Galilei, abolished forever the concept of an earth-centered universe. Galileo, in the early 17th century, discovered four bodies that orbited Jupiter — not the resplendent central earth.

Half a century after Galileo's discovery, the Englishman Sir Isaac Newton used precise mathematics to state fundamental laws of motion and gravitation that applied equally to the fall of an apple and the movement of a planet. Orbital motion, said Newton, is the result of the balancing of two powerful forces: centrifugal force tending to

cause a revolving body to continue on into space in a straight line, and gravitation tending to attract the revolving body.

Newton's later discovery that sunlight is the combination of many colors led to the spectroscope, through which astronomers were to discover not only the composition of heavenly bodies but also the approximate speeds at which they moved. In spectrographic portraits of distant galaxies, the displacement in their wave lengths, called the "red shift," tells us that the farther galaxies are away from earth, the faster they are receding from us.

The road from Newton to Albert Einstein was

paved with new methods of mathematical analysis and brilliant refinements in the techniques and discoveries of observational astronomy. In his Special Theory of Relativity, presented in a paper published in 1905, Einstein theorized that the velocity of light remains constant with respect to the motion of any body in the universe. His theory embraced a finite universe in which everything—matter and energy, space and time—is included and interrelated.

In regard to the universe as a whole, Einstein provided the basis for what came to be known as "the cosmological question." Did the universe begin with a "big bang," and is the universe still expanding? Did it evolve gradually, as stars and galaxies condensed from vast clouds of gas? Some scientists said "no." They believed that the universe is in a "steady state," not expanding at all. The density of matter and space, they contended, remains constant in time.

Another and smaller group looked for answers closer to home among the nine planets: Mercury, Venus, Earth, Mars, Jupiter, Saturn, Uranus, Neptune, and cold, dark, and distant Pluto.

Until 1781 only the first six planets were known. In that year William Herschel of England discovered a seventh—Uranus. A few years later scientists applied Newton's law of gravitation to

Uranus after they had noticed it deviated from its predicted orbit. Perhaps, they reasoned, Uranus was affected by the gravitational pull of an unknown planet. Astronomers determined the position of the mysterious force that caused Uranus' erratic behavior, and in 1846 discovered the eighth planet, Neptune.

Neptune, too, showed fascinating orbital deviations. One day in 1930, a young assistant named Clyde Tombaugh was working in the Lowell Observatory among the ponderosa pines of Flagstaff, Arizona. Hunched over a device used for comparing photographs, he carefully studied pictures of the skies taken several nights apart. His purpose was to see if any one of thousands of specks of light had changed position. Such an occurrence would mean that he had spotted "Planet X," then the object of a worldwide search.

Suddenly Tombaugh leaned forward. A single dot appeared to have moved. He quickly examined other plates. The tiny speck seemed to be traveling through space. Heart pounding, Tombaugh strode down the hall and entered the office of his superior, Dr. V. M. Slipher. Three years earlier Dr. Slipher had been so impressed with drawings of Mars that Tombaugh had made with the help of his homemade telescope that he sent a letter to the Kansas wheat farm where Tombaugh lived and offered him a job.

"Dr. Slipher," Tombaugh announced, "I've found Planet X." The Kansas farm boy had indeed discovered the ninth planet, Pluto.

I once talked with Clyde Tombaugh after he moved to Las Cruces to teach at New Mexico State University. He pointed proudly to a 16-inch telescope he had built in his back yard.

"For 14 years," he explained to me somewhat ruefully, "I searched the skies for a possible tenth planet, but I finally concluded that Pluto is our last one."

What does Tombaugh use his telescope for today? He trains it on Mars and sometimes on projected impact points on the moon. He hopes to be the first man to see a lunar probe strike the moon's surface.

With the discovery of our final planet, which, predictably, behaved according to the laws of Kepler and Newton, man's physical model of the solar system was essentially complete.

At about the same time we were able to comprehend a solar system of nine planets, a new, little-known branch of science — that of rocketry — began to emerge, stimulated in part by science-fiction accounts through the years.

Fictional journeys into space, though often depending upon such unorthodox means of locomotion as geese, swans, demons, and chariots, employed rocket principles as early as the 17th century. In *Voyages to the Moon and the Sun,* Cyrano de Bergerac introduced a "machine" powered by rockets. Igniting in quick succession, the rockets boosted de Bergerac "into the clouds."

Ironically, the great astronomer and mathematician Kepler, when he turned from space science to space fiction, used highly unscientific methods. He solved the problem of propulsion by having demons magically transport human beings to the moon during times of eclipse.

MUSIC MASTER AND ASTRONOMER, *William Herschel discovered Uranus in 1781 while studying the sky as a hobby. The German-born immigrant to England named his find the Georgian Planet after King George III; later he became the court astronomer.*

BOATLOAD *of gaily dressed space travelers returns from the moon by parachute, bringing captured lunar creatures and weird plants. This 19th-century print reflects the belief of Herschel and others of his day that life existed on the moon.*

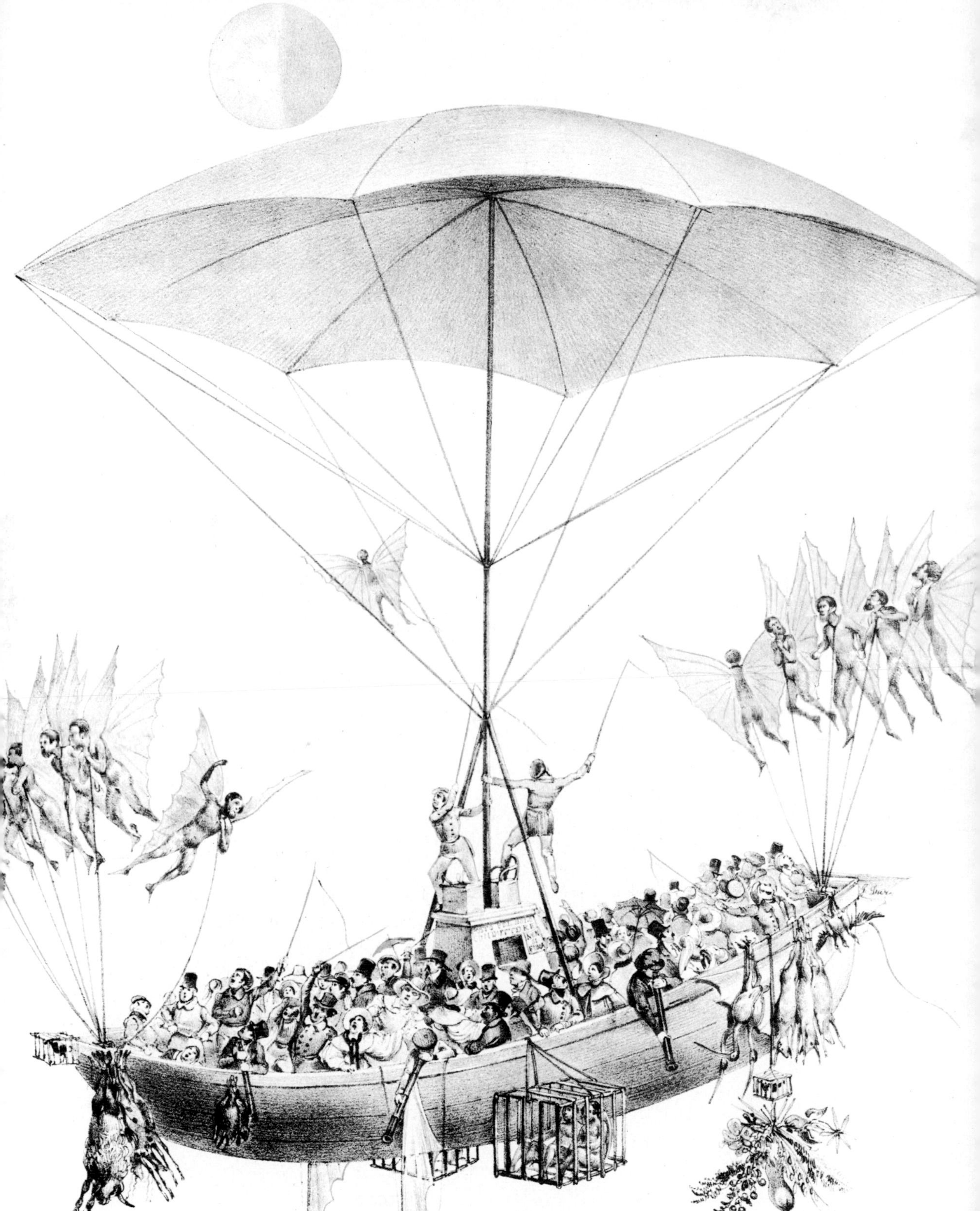

The Frenchman Jules Verne, whose prophetic writings in the 1860's influenced pioneer rocket scientists of the 20th century, developed the concept of steering-rockets to maneuver his spaceship in *From the Earth to the Moon* and in *Around the Moon*. The ship's initial impetus was delivered by a 900-foot-long cannon buried upright in Florida sands. However, the rapid acceleration necessary to propel the rocket into space would have killed the three-man crew instantly.

Around the beginning of the 20th century, H. G. Wells conceived a system of propulsion that was simplicity itself. In *The First Men in the Moon,* his spacemen entered a sphere enameled with a mysterious gravity-defying substance called "Cavorite," opened a window aimed at the moon, and sped on their way.

Wells devised the idea of Cavorite at about the time it became clear that the Chinese, who had invented gunpowder and rockets centuries earlier, were on the right track all along; rocket propulsion was the practical means of sending into space cargoes of explosives, instruments, and human life itself.

The basic principle applied by the Chinese to launch their rockets has been observed by children for generations: A toy balloon expelling air provides a simple example of rocket propulsion. So does a firecracker that misfires and fizzles across the sidewalk, spewing smoke.

The Chinese and Mongols improved multiple arrows of "flying fire." Propelled by rockets, the missiles rushed out "on a solid front like 100 tigers." The Mongols carried the new rocket weapons to the Near East and ultimately to Europe. By the 16th century many Europeans had become fascinated with the "casing that flies" and with its potential both in fireworks displays and in warfare. In 1668 a German field artillery colonel, Christoph Friedrich von Geissler, developed and fired several successful experimental rockets weighing up to 132 pounds.

Military rocket development proceeded rapidly in 19th-century Europe. More than 25,000 British rockets developed by Col. William Congreve were launched against Copenhagen in 1807. The same type of rocket, weighing about 30 pounds, was later used in the War of 1812. Francis Scott Key's words, "the rockets' red glare" in "The Star-Spangled Banner" refer to the British rockets launched during the bombardment of Baltimore's Fort McHenry.

In World War I, rockets were used chiefly to launch signal and parachute flares that illuminated enemy positions at night. The French made limited use of rockets, firing them from Nieuport biplanes at barrage balloons and from the ground at German Zeppelins. But, generally speaking, military rockets of the period were made nearly obsolete by improved artillery, the airplane, and radio—which in England saw experimental use as a means of directing a pilotless plane or "flying bomb" to a target.

If rocket applications were somewhat limited, rocket theory was slowly emerging with a few isolated, highly imaginative, but practical individuals who were to influence profoundly the coming age of space. The first of these was the Russian, Konstantin Tsiolkovsky.

On a trip to the Soviet Union in 1966, I asked authorities if I could visit Kaluga, where Tsiolkovsky worked in his later years. In a little Volga car, I drove to the railroad and machinery city on the banks of the Oka River some 125 miles from Moscow. Tsiolkovsky's grandson, Alexei Kostin, showed me the tools, models, and papers of his distinguished grandfather.

At the age of nine, according to Alexei Kostin, an attack of scarlet fever severely impaired Tsiolkovsky's hearing. Virtually shut off from the world of sound, his mind turned inward and dreamed.

"In my imagination," Tsiolkovsky wrote of his childhood, "I could jump higher than anybody else, climbed poles like a cat and walked ropes. I dreamed . . . there was no such thing as gravity."

After educating himself in mathematics and physics, Tsiolkovsky experimented with gravity-defying contraptions ranging from a "mechanical hawk" to balloons and an all-metal dirigible. Barely supporting himself on a teacher's stipend, he worked with increasing attention on the theory of

ALBERT EINSTEIN *revolutionized man's concepts of space, time, matter, energy, and light half a century before the first orbital flight. At age 26, he stated in his theory of relativity that all of these are not independent of one another, but complexly interrelated. The physicist's famous equation, $E=mc^2$ (energy equals mass times the speed of light squared), led to the production of nuclear energy, which may someday power space ships.*

space flight. Stimulated by fantasy writer Jules Verne, Tsiolkovsky wrote:

"To place one's feet on the soil of asteroids, to lift a stone from the moon with your hand, to construct moving stations in ether space ... to observe Mars at the distance of several tens of miles, to descend to its satellites or even to its own surface—what could be more insane! However, only at such a time when reactive devices are applied, will a new great era begin in astronomy: the era of more intensive study of the heavens."

In 1903 he published in *Scientific Review* his first article on rocketry, a theoretically sound primer on the liquid-propellant rocket such as the models I saw in his workshop. Later, he improved his drawings and explanations of rockets, of the use of kerosene as a fuel, of methods of cooling the combustion chamber, of various means of guidance, and of the multistage rocket, or what he called a rocket train.

By the age of 78, he had written scores of scientific papers and a number of science-fiction novels, but he still devoted half of his time, as he put it, "to the problem of overcoming terrestrial gravity and making flights into space."

Two years before his death in 1935, he made a prophetic declaration on a radio broadcast: ". . . I am firmly convinced that my ... dream—space travel . . . will be realized. . . . I believe that many of you will be witnesses of the first journey beyond the atmosphere. . . ."

The father of modern rocketry in America, Robert H. Goddard, was born on October 5, 1882, in Worcester, Massachusetts. As early as high school, he was writing papers on space, and by the time he received his doctorate from Clark University in Worcester in 1911, he had already discovered, as Tsiolkovsky did, that liquid oxygen and liquid hydrogen would make an ideal rocket propellant. Within four years, Goddard had carried out several successful field experiments, including the launch of powder rockets that rose as high as

486 feet above the Massachusetts countryside.

In 1917 the Smithsonian Institution granted him $5,000 to conduct high-altitude experiments. Two years later, a paper on his proposal, "A Method of Reaching Extreme Altitudes," was published, presenting a type of propulsion that theoretically could send a rocket to the moon. Goddard incidentally included a method of determining whether the rocket had reached its target: On impact, a mass of flash powder attached to the missile would explode and could be observed from earth by telescope.

The relatively insignificant flash powder idea, not the rocket theory, caught the public fancy.

The quiet, mustached professor found himself the object of popular attention. Thereafter shunning publicity, he alternated between his own rocket research and work on depth charges and armor-piercing rocket projectiles for the U. S. Navy in the early 1920's.

In March of 1926, a 12-foot projectile, the world's first liquid-propellant rocket, rose from the farm of Robert Goddard's Aunt Effie near Auburn, Massachusetts. The short flight, before the engine malfunctioned, was reminiscent of Kitty Hawk: height 41 feet; distance 184 feet; speed 60 miles per hour. Goddard sent up three more rockets at Auburn. The last, on July 17, 1929, was mistaken by residents for an airplane in flames, and the incident caused a flood of publicity.

From some of the newspaper accounts, Col. Charles A. Lindbergh learned of Goddard and his work and paid him a surprise visit in November. The great aviator, like Goddard, envisioned an expanding future of rocket travel and, ultimately, space flight. Lindbergh encouraged philanthropist Daniel Guggenheim to grant Goddard $100,000.

With four assistants, Goddard set up a simple rocket launch facility near Roswell, New Mexico. There he lived and breathed rockets for more than a decade. In 1935 he launched a remarkably sophisticated 85-pound projectile. Its liquid oxygen

and gasoline were fed into a combustion chamber from a pressurized tank; the chamber itself was prevented from melting by the flow of propellants within its hollow casing—a procedure called "curtain cooling"; a gyroscope provided in-flight stability. The rocket rose 7,500 feet above the New Mexico desert. Another reached almost supersonic speed.

With continued financial support from The Daniel and Florence Guggenheim Foundation, Goddard built and flew dozens of intricate rockets while living in New Mexico. However, he was far better known abroad than in his own country. In Germany scientists used many of the same engineering principles as Goddard, in creating the V-2 rocket that was launched by the thousand against Allied targets during World War II.

Germany was not without its own pioneer in the theory of rocket flight. The early calculations and writings of a blue-eyed professor of mathematics and physics named Hermann Oberth certainly must rank him along with Tsiolkovsky as a major rocket theoretician.

"At the age of eleven," Oberth reveals in his autobiography, "I received from my mother as a gift the famous books . . . by Jules Verne, which I read at least five or six times and, finally, knew by heart."

FREDERICK I. ORDWAY III

GUNPOWDER ROCKETS, used by the British against Napoleon, arch above the battlefield at Waterloo on June 18, 1815, as a charging column of French horsemen attacks unwavering ranks of British foot soldiers. Rockets found use as weapons of war as early as the 13th century in both Europe and the Orient. At left, Sir William Congreve, developer of war rockets for Britain, watches Copenhagen go up in flames after a fierce incendiary barrage in 1807. Congreve's rockets saw their most celebrated moment in the British bombardment of Baltimore's Fort McHenry on the night of September 13, 1814, during the War of 1812, when Francis Scott Key immortalized "the rockets' red glare" in verse.

45

While in his 20's, during World War I, Oberth unsuccessfully proposed liquid-propellant long-range bombardment missiles to the German War Department. Later, after learning of Goddard's work from a newspaper account, Oberth corresponded with him, suggesting that they exchange their writings. "I think that only by the common work of scholars of all nations," Oberth wrote, "can be solved this great problem . . . to pass over the atmosphere of our earth by means of a rocket."

In 1923, Oberth published a thin but highly influential book called *The Rocket into Planetary Space,* in which he provided an enlightened and practical design for a complex liquid-propellant rocket to explore the upper atmosphere. Six years later, he published a 423-page expansion, *The Road To Space Travel.* The same year he became president of Germany's Society for Space Travel.

Oberth, hoping to stimulate public interest in his field, consented to launch a rocket for a German movie. The attempt failed but attracted widespread attention, especially from Germany's growing roster of young rocket enthusiasts. The German-born author, Dieter K. Huzel, wrote of this period, "As model airplanes captured the enthusiasm of American youngsters in the 1930's, so rockets were a source of endless excitement, and an even more challenging toy, for German children of the 1920's."

In 1932, the Society for Space Travel moved to the Kummersdorf proving ground near Berlin to test rockets. Among early members of the group was a handsome, firm-jawed student named Wernher von Braun and a young engineer, Walter Dornberger, who persuaded the German army to donate a modest sum to finance test flights. By 1934, eight years after Goddard fired his first liquid-fueled rocket, the Germans got two such projectiles to an altitude of 6,500 feet. By 1937, despite the financial depression in Germany, the

SHUTTLING PASSENGERS *to the moon, a coal-burning missile (opposite) speeds through space on a fanciful voyage inspired by the writings of Frenchman Jules Verne. In his 1865 classic,* From the Earth to the Moon, *a "spout of fire" from a buried cannon launched a space capsule. In a sequel,* Around the Moon, *Verne anticipated the effects of weightlessness on space travelers. The author, amazingly prophetic, had his moon ship zoom skyward only 120 miles west of present-day Cape Kennedy.*

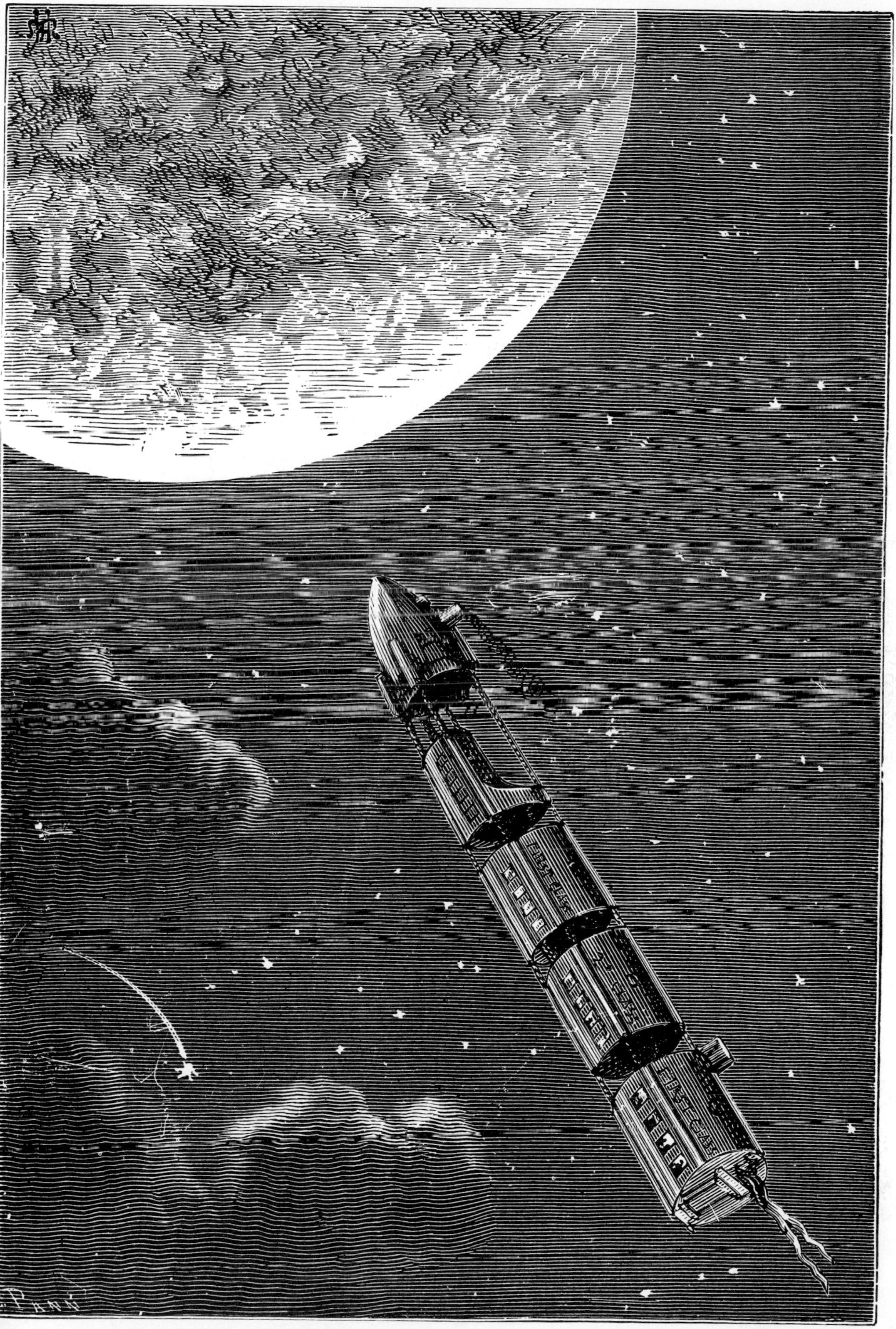

Dornberger-von Braun group numbered nearly a hundred and had expanded activities to a new test site on the Baltic coast called Peenemünde.

In Russia, by the early 1930's, government-backed scientists in Leningrad and Moscow were already gaining team experience in building and testing solid- and liquid-fueled rocket motors. By the mid-1930's, Russian rockets were reaching altitudes of up to 3.5 miles. Around 1940, the Russians developed a rocket with a 12-mile range, using a combination of solid and liquid propellants.

By then all three countries had suffered temporary setbacks. Goddard postponed his work to assist in military research projects. In Moscow's suspicious and sensitive political atmosphere, expanding Soviet rocket societies became suspect. And Germany's capricious chancellor, Adolf Hitler, dreamed one night that missiles wouldn't reach England, and for a time withheld development funds. But despite the shortage of money, the German army continued its work on rockets.

The advent of World War II brought about a resurgence of rockets of all types, surface-to-air, air-to-air, and air-to-surface. These included batteries of comparatively small solid-propellant rockets which both the German and Russian armies fired at each other in barrage fashion.

The United States employed a number of rocket arms; one of the best known was the bazooka, a shoulder-held grenade launcher inspired by Robert Goddard. The air forces of all combatants developed both jet and rocket engines to give an added boost to heavily loaded planes at takeoff.

But it was the supersecret products that rose

M/SGT. G. B. GILBERT AND CAPT. H. K. BAISLEY (ABOVE) AND THE BELL FAMILY

LIFTING MAN *to the stratosphere,* Explorer II *rises above South Dakota on a mission sponsored in 1935 by the National Geographic Society and the U. S. Army Air Corps. The balloon reached an altitude of 13.71 miles—a record that stood for 21 years. Decades earlier, in 1893, Dr. Alexander Graham Bell (right), experimenting with new propellants, built a rocket-powered model aircraft that flew 75 feet. The notation on his sketch warns against blast that might buckle the thin metal tail.*

RUSSIAN THEORIST *Konstantin Tsiolkovsky (left), first to suggest the use of rockets for space travel, studies at his home in Kaluga. In the early 1900's Tsiolkovsky advanced the idea that powerful rockets could escape the earth's gravitational pull.*

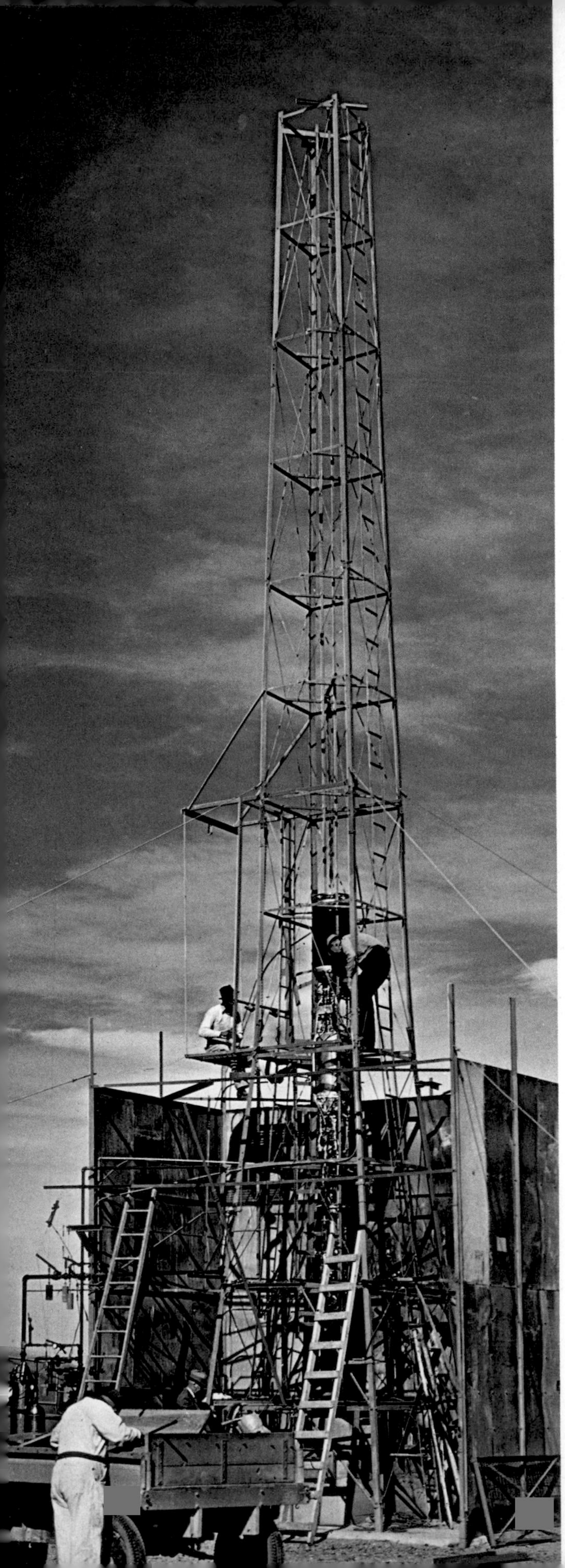

COURTESY ESTHER C. GODDARD (LEFT)

NATIONAL GEOGRAPHIC PHOTOGRAPHER B. ANTHONY STEWART (ABOVE AND RIGHT)

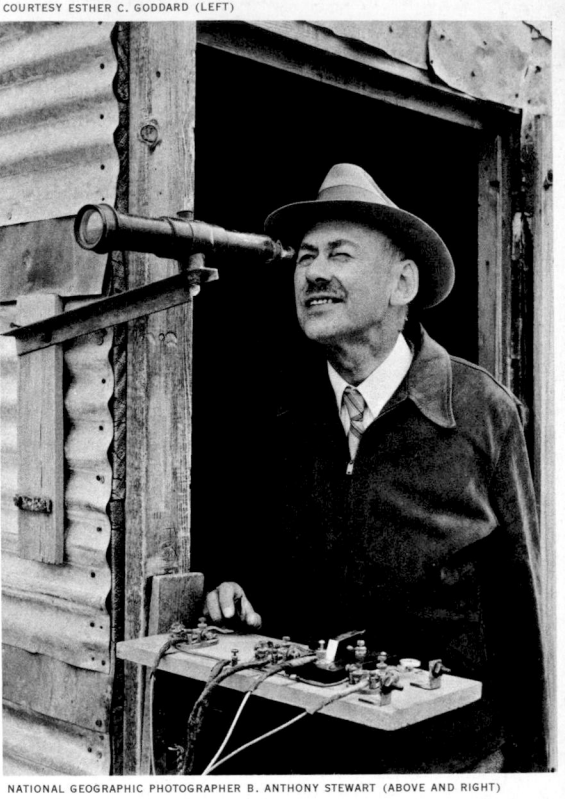

PIONEER OF MODERN ROCKETRY, *American Robert H. Goddard keeps a finger on the ignition key as he sights the launch tower at Eden Valley, New Mexico, in 1940. Combining theory and practice, Goddard created the first rockets to use liquid oxygen and gasoline as fuel. Crewmen at left prepare a rocket for firing. At right, Goddard inspects one of his test projectiles on its assembly frame.*

from the Peenemünde development pads that gave rocketry its most astonishing thrust. From 1938 on, the Dornberger-von Braun group tested a succession of liquid-fueled rockets. In 1943, Hitler, in his desperate search for *wunder-waffen* —wonder weapons—finally decided to give top priority to the gasoline-burning V-1 "buzz bomb," and the 46-foot V-2 ballistic rocket.

By 1944, the first of more than 4,000 V-2's were launched. With a speed of 3,600 miles per hour, a range of up to 200 miles, and a ton of explosives, the V-2 quickly proved it was a true "wonder weapon" against which there was no known defense. Flaming alcohol and liquid oxygen pushed it skyward. Once its engine shut down, it arched through the edge of space to its target. Its deadly payload then plunged downward much too fast for interception.

The V-2, combining the best concepts of Tsiolkovsky, Goddard, and Oberth, represented by far

the most brilliant single forward stride thus far taken in rocketry.

Although born as a weapon of war, the V-2 represented much more than that to the rocket scientists; it was an exciting new means of transportation, like the steamship, the railroad, and the airplane, whose future cargo could include everything from mail to human beings. And most important, of all means of transportation, it, alone, was unconfined by the atmosphere of earth.

At war's end, Peenemünde held the most significant war booty of modern times. But when the Russians reached the site, they found a few rockets and little else. Unknown to them, von Braun and his colleagues had voted to turn over their knowledge to the Americans. As the heart of the Peenemünde technical team moved south before the advancing Russians, they led a curious convoy of trucks and trailers. Inside the trucks reposed the key plans and blueprints not only of the V-2 but of even larger rockets capable of transatlantic flight.

Dieter Huzel, who cautiously shepherded the precious trucks, later wrote in his book *Peenemünde to Canaveral,* "These documents were of inestimable value. Whoever inherited them would be able to start in rocketry at that point at which we had left off, with the benefit not only of our accomplishments, but of our mistakes as well — the real ingredient of experience. They represented years of intensive effort in a brand-new technology, one which, all of us were still convinced, would play a profound role in the future course of human events."

GERMAN V-2 ROCKETS *crowd a production depot at Nordhausen in World War II. Riding a narrow-gauge track, a missile passes beneath a no-smoking sign, bound for one of scores of launching sites. More than 4,000 of the projectiles, perfected late in the war at Peenemünde, roared toward Allied targets at 3,600 miles an hour. German pioneer Hermann Oberth (left), who believed rockets could launch vehicles into space, inspired experimentation that led to the V-2. Below, 18-year-old Werner von Braun, a student of Oberth's, carries an experimental rocket at a Berlin testing ground in 1930.*

37
11/W 4156

11/W 4171

Rauchen verboten.

3/ DANGERS OF THE COSMOS BEYOND EARTH'S COCOON

Astronaut Charles ("Pete") Conrad, Jr., and I had obviously not been alone in our decision to go for a Sunday-afternoon skyride. As we swooped toward the airfield near Houston's Manned Spacecraft Center, a swarm of small planes seemed to fill the air, darting like bees above a field of clover. Shoving the throttle forward, Pete shook his head and quickly nosed the light plane toward less-crowded skies. "Give me space!" he shouted. "I'll take space any day!"

For a brief moment I wondered which "space" he was thinking about, the peaceful roominess we were now enjoying less than a mile above the coastal plain, or the 850-mile height he reached with fellow astronaut Richard F. Gordon in September, 1966. Heading for a landing, Pete answered my unspoken question with a side glance and a quick grin. It was the same exuberant expression television viewers saw after the splashdown of Gemini 11. "This has got to be the greatest ride in the world," he later told reporters.

In his trip above the atmosphere, Conrad had done what scientists over the centuries have wished to do—observe the earth at a point away from its surface and, without the distorting effects of the atmosphere, study the other planets, the sun, and the vastly more distant stars glowing in the depths of space.

Now rockets have made such trips, such observations possible. Pete Conrad and Dick Gordon left the earth on top of Titan II, one of the most powerful rockets the United States had in 1966, a far cry from the V-2's of the 1940's and the not always reliable rockets of the 1950's. The Titan II was the latest of a string of memorable names in U. S. rocket development: Vanguard, Redstone, Jupiter, Thor, Atlas—used for America's first manned orbital flights—and the mighty Saturn.

The Titan II was powered by stored liquid chemicals that ignited spontaneously when mixed. Its first stage produced 430,000 pounds of thrust to lift the 109-foot rocket off the ground; the second

STARS TRACE *circular pastel paths around the brightly shining North Star, and a meteor streaks across the atmosphere during a two-hour time exposure taken at the U. S. Naval Observatory in Washington, D. C. Probing into space with telescope, camera, and satellite, man investigates the relationships of the earth, the solar system, and the universe.*

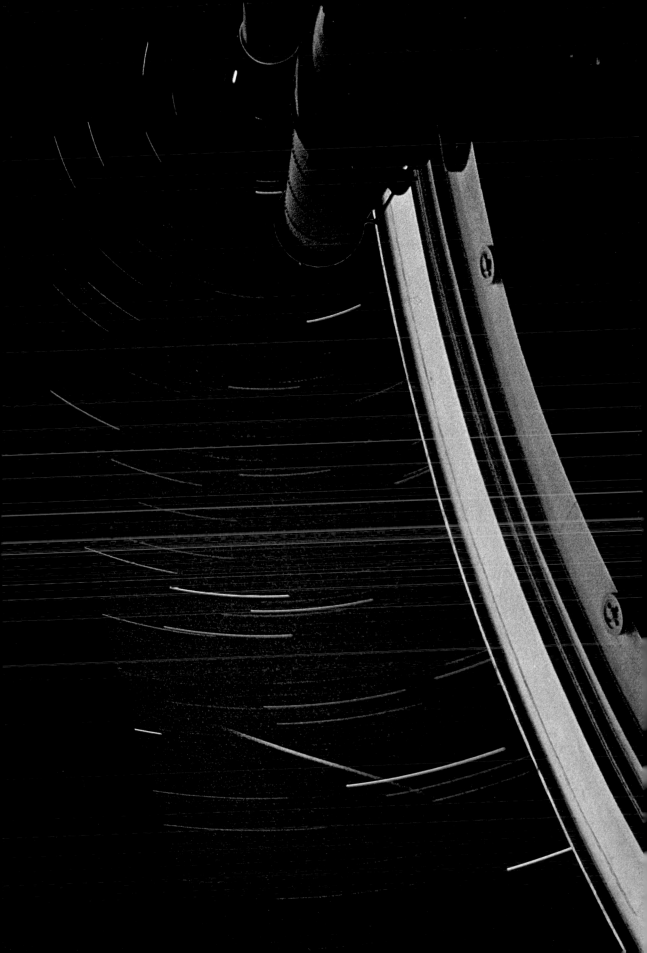

DR. SYUN-ICHI AKASOFU

stage fired in space and sent Conrad and Gordon into their first orbit 165 miles high.

Within five minutes after lift-off, the astronauts had left behind the face-distorting super-gravity created by rapid acceleration, and were traveling weightlessly around the earth at 17,500 miles an hour. Their flight speed maintained an outward force equal to the pull of gravity, holding them in an orbital track. If they had stepped out of their spacecraft untethered, they too would have become separate orbiting celestial objects whose course Newton could have described with a mathematical equation.

When the astronauts came back to earth after three days, they had felt and seen proof of the physical laws of space in operation at the greatest height man had yet attained. Closer to the stars than any man before him, Gordon had hung out the open hatch of the craft, taking pictures of celestial bodies, photographing our own sun as it poured energy on a turning earth.

How easily we forget, down here under our protective blanket of air, that our sun is a nuclear holocaust! Every second it transforms some four million tons of its matter into electromagnetic energy that streams into space. Fragments of atoms boil off the sun's surface at high speeds. The rays travel at 671 million miles an hour—186,000 miles per second—across space; the atomic fragments move more slowly and create a solar wind that sweeps about the planets as they orbit the sun.

Only about one two-billionths of the sun's radiation reaches us, but if we had no protection, especially during great outbursts, or flares, on the sun, the rays and fragments would create a sizzling, deadly environment on earth. Fortunately, two lines of defense surround the earth—a magnetic field and the atmosphere.

The sun's rays—visible light, invisible infrared, ultraviolet, radio waves, and X-rays—reach us first. They take only eight minutes to speed the 93 million miles to earth. The slower solar wind protons (hydrogen nuclei), electrons, and scraps of other elements normally arrive in four days, but during a flare, they come in eight to 24 hours.

Surrounding earth in layers like the concentric sections of an onion, the magnetic field holds off or interrupts many of the particles. The invisible lines of force forming the layers originate at the earth's magnetic core, believed to be a molten mass of nickel-iron. North-south magnetic lines sweep out from earth in majestic arcs, the outer ones reaching 40,000 miles into space.

"On the side toward the sun, the powerful field deflects most of the particles of the solar wind, causing them to flow along the boundary of the

earth's magnetic field," says physicist Donald J. Williams, of Goddard Space Flight Center. "On the side away from the sun the field stretches out like a tail or the wake of a ship far beyond the orbit of the moon. The solar wind flow," Dr. Williams adds, "sets up mechanisms, not yet fully understood, which are responsible for the now familiar Van Allen radiation belt. The band encircles the earth opposite the middle latitudes where most people live. No one knew of the belt until Geiger counters on the first U. S. unmanned satellites, Explorer I and III, revealed concentrations of amazingly high radiation counts."

Conrad and Gordon in their Gemini spacecraft penetrated the lower fringe of the region. Instruments on board measured radiation and confirmed earlier findings by satellites that men inside a craft passing quickly through the band of radiation would not be harmed.

A few particles are lost from the trap and rush into our atmosphere. They collide with air molecules, lose speed, and become part of the atmosphere. In the polar regions where the Van Allen belt does not reach, great quantities of the particles from distant regions of the magnetosphere may fly in along the outer lines of the magnetic field. Like

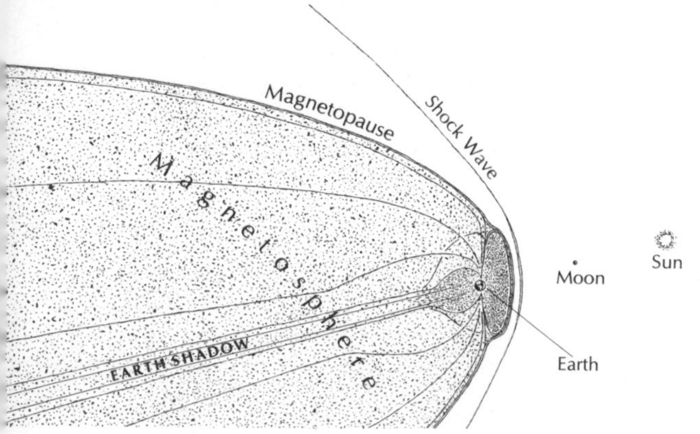

Magnetopause

Shock Wave

Magnetosphere

EARTH SHADOW

Moon

Sun

Earth

VAST, INVISIBLE SHIELD, the magnetosphere (shown in cross section and indicated by stippled purple and green areas) envelops earth, protecting man from solar and galactic radiation. This gigantic envelope results from the collision of earth's magnetic field with the solar wind—a continuous blast of electrons and protons emitted by the sun. The boundary of the magnetosphere, the magnetopause, occurs where the pressure of the magnetic field equals that of the solar wind. This point represents the closest approach of the wind to earth,

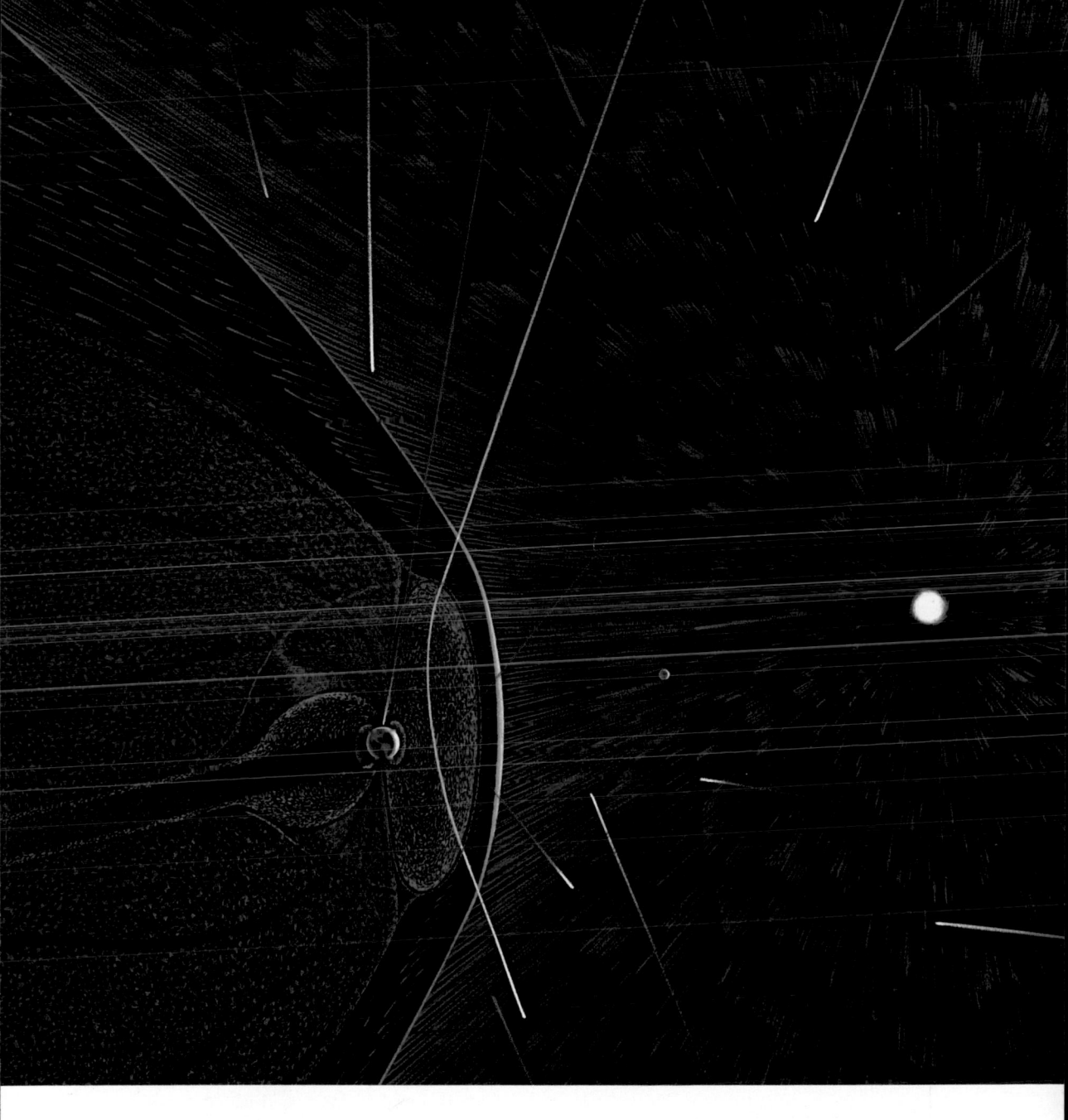

some 40,000 miles in the direction of the sun. The solar wind, unable to penetrate closer to earth, flows along the magnetopause and defines the cavity containing earth's magnetic field. The part of this field originating in the polar regions of the earth is pushed back by the wind and trails out more than a million miles, forming the magnetic tail. At the unprotected polar caps, solar and galactic cosmic rays—orange and yellow streaks —easily penetrate to the atmosphere. The collision of the solar wind with earth's magnetic field

produces a shock wave (bowed blue line) 15,000 miles in front of the magnetopause in the direction of the sun. Trapped charged particles encircle earth, forming the Van Allen radiation belt (in green). Scientists at first believed the belt had two layers, but satellites later revealed one band. It extends 40,000 miles beyond earth, with heaviest concentrations of protons and electrons at 1,500 and 15,000 miles. The moon, lacking a magnetic field or atmosphere like earth's, gets full exposure to solar radiation on its sunward side.

a heavy rain, they pour into the upper atmosphere near the poles and collide with air molecules. The collisions produce the dramatic shimmering curtains of color we call auroras.

But how are we protected from the solar rays—ultraviolet and X-rays that have short, extremely energetic wave lengths? They pass through our magnetic field unhindered, for its lines of force can ensnare only electrically charged particles. Like a wall, our atmosphere blocks them. The rays pass through hundreds of miles of this gradually thickening zone. Those with the shortest wave lengths use up their dangerous energy as they shatter the "bricks"—air molecules—and chip

electrons from atoms, changing them into ions, or charged particles. The region of ions and free electrons, called the ionosphere, not only protects man from solar radiation, but it also serves as a reflector for long-distance radio-communication waves.

Still the danger from rays is not completely over. Below the ionosphere, at an altitude of about 30 miles, another crucial defender waits: Molecules of ozone, a form of oxygen, absorb the energy of potent ultraviolet rays of long wave lengths. Finally the stratosphere and the dense troposphere, which holds the air we breathe, soak up most of the energy of other rays and particles, letting through only life-giving light, benign radio waves,

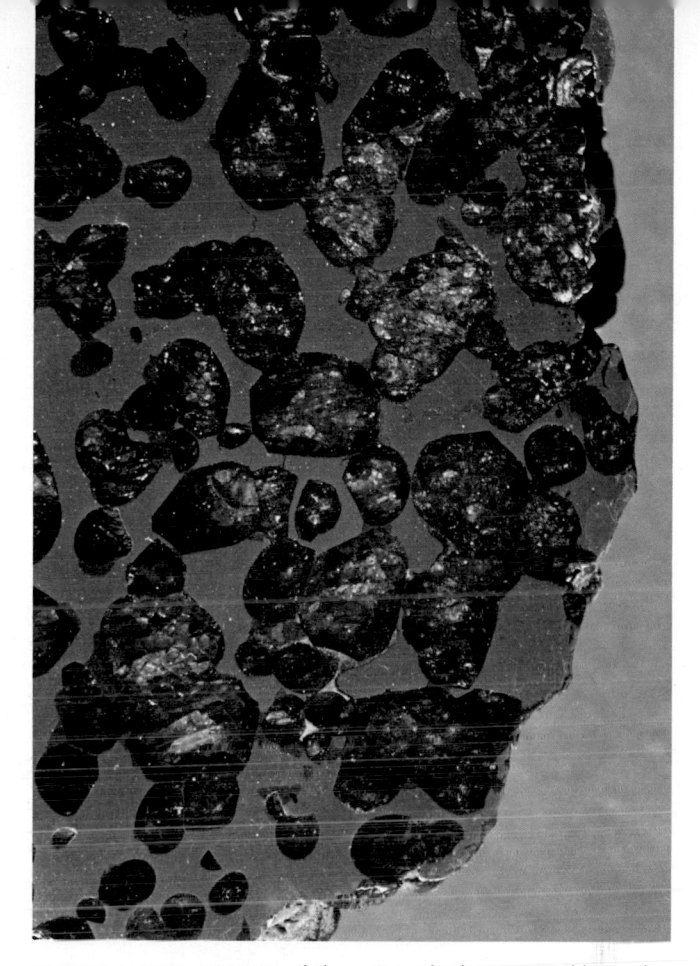

TIGHTLY PACKED CRYSTALS of the mineral olivine sparkle in this cross section of a pallasite meteorite. A metallic core of nickel-iron surrounds the crystals. In Arizona's Oak Creek Canyon, meteoriticist H. H. Nininger pauses outside his home during the 162-hour operation of sawing through the one-ton Bondoc meteorite, brought to the U. S. from the Philippines. More than 20,000 years ago, a 63,000-ton meteorite blasted out Arizona's three-quarter-mile-wide Meteor Crater. The material of meteorites, distributed throughout the solar system, may represent the original state of matter that formed the planets.

WILLIAM BELKNAP, JR. (ABOVE AND UPPER RIGHT) AND HAL G. STEPHENS, U. S. GEOLOGICAL SURVEY

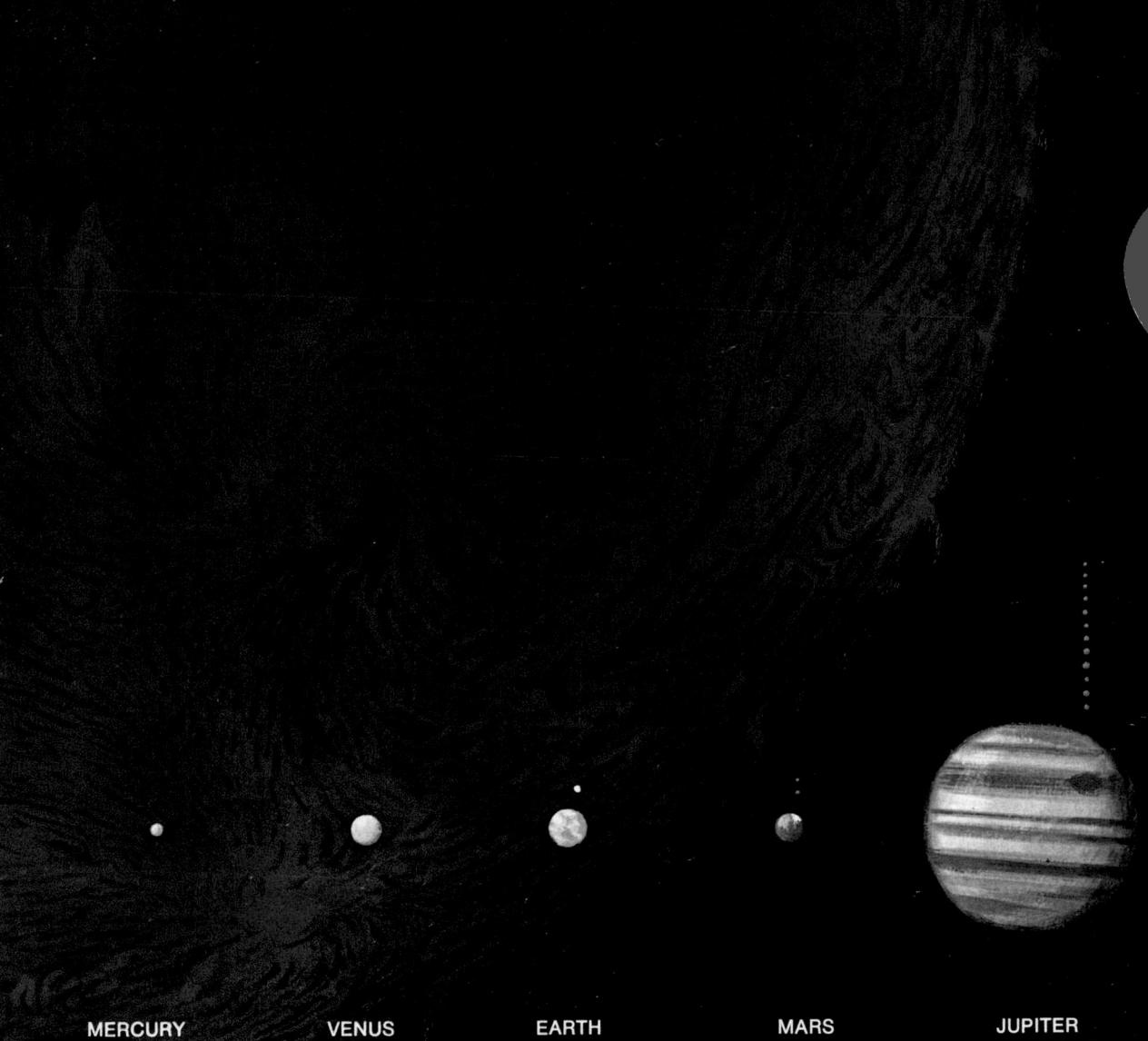

MERCURY	VENUS	EARTH	MARS	JUPITER
Diameter: 3,010 miles	Diameter: 7,525 miles	Diameter: 7,926 miles	Diameter: 4,240 miles	Diameter: 88,670 miles
Distance from sun: 36 million miles	Distance from sun: 67.2 million miles	Distance from sun: 93 million miles	Distance from sun: 141.5 million miles	Distance from sun: 484 million miles
Period of solar orbit: 88 days*	Period of solar orbit: 224.7 days	Period of solar orbit: 365.3 days	Period of solar orbit: 1.88 years	Period of solar orbit: 11.9 years
Rotation period: 59 days	Rotation period: 243.1 days	Rotation period: 23.9 hours	Rotation period: 24.6 hours	Rotation period: 9.9 hours
		Moons: 1	Moons: 2	Moons: 12

*All times expressed by earth standards

DOMINATING OUR SOLAR SYSTEM, *the massive sun holds nine planets in orbit with its powerful gravitational force. This typical star, more than a million times larger than the earth, contains 99.86 percent of the solar system's matter. Planets—from the Greek word for wanderers—divide into two groups according to their properties. Mercury, Venus, Earth, Mars, and possibly distant Pluto, make up the terrestrial planets, composed of nickel-iron and a mixture of rocky materials. Hydrogen and helium form the bulk of the larger and more massive Jovian planets—Jupiter, Saturn, Uranus, and Neptune. The orbital velocities of the planets vary greatly with respect to their distances from the sun: Tiny Mercury hurtles around its stellar neighbor at*

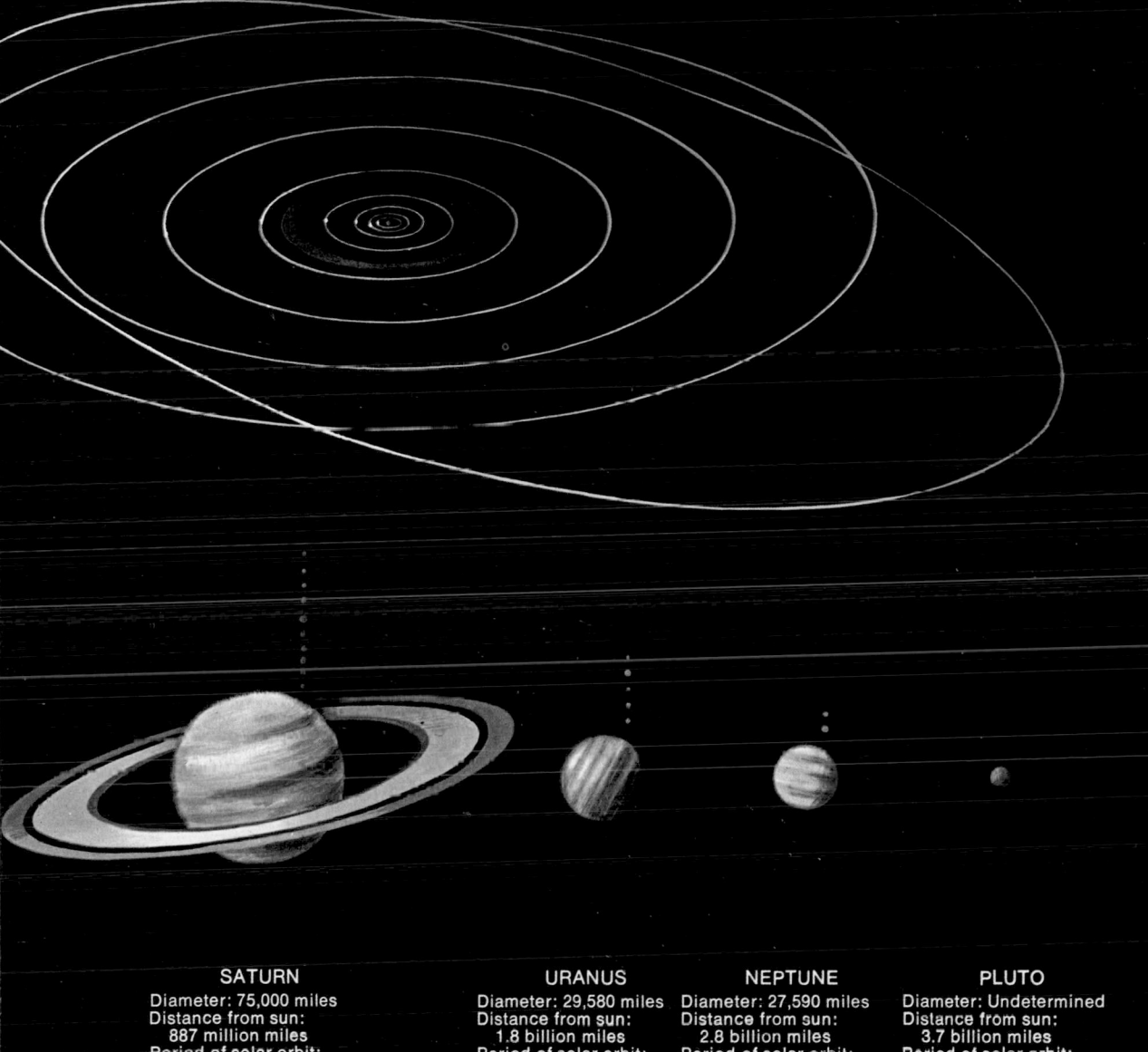

SATURN	URANUS	NEPTUNE	PLUTO
Diameter: 75,000 miles	Diameter: 29,580 miles	Diameter: 27,590 miles	Diameter: Undetermined
Distance from sun:	Distance from sun:	Distance from sun:	Distance from sun:
887 million miles	1.8 billion miles	2.8 billion miles	3.7 billion miles
Period of solar orbit:	Period of solar orbit:	Period of solar orbit:	Period of solar orbit:
29.5 years	84 years	164.8 years	248.4 years
Rotation period:	Rotation period:	Rotation period:	Rotation period:
10.3 hours	10.7 hours	15.8 hours	6.4 days
Moons: 10	Moons: 5	Moons: 2	

*110,000 miles an hour; Pluto crawls at one-tenth that speed. A total of 32
moons orbit six of the planets. The asteroid belt (brown band in diagram
above), holding more than 50,000 chunks of planetary material with
diameters up to 470 miles, rings the sun between the orbits of Mars and
Jupiter. Some scientists speculate that these planetoids once made up a
larger planet, now fragmented. Others believe that the particles never
had a chance to coalesce into a planet because Jupiter's heavy gravitational pull kept them scattered. Except for Pluto, inclined more than 17°,
the planets orbit the sun in approximately the same plane (above). This
oblique-angle view exaggerates the slightly elliptical paths of the planets.*

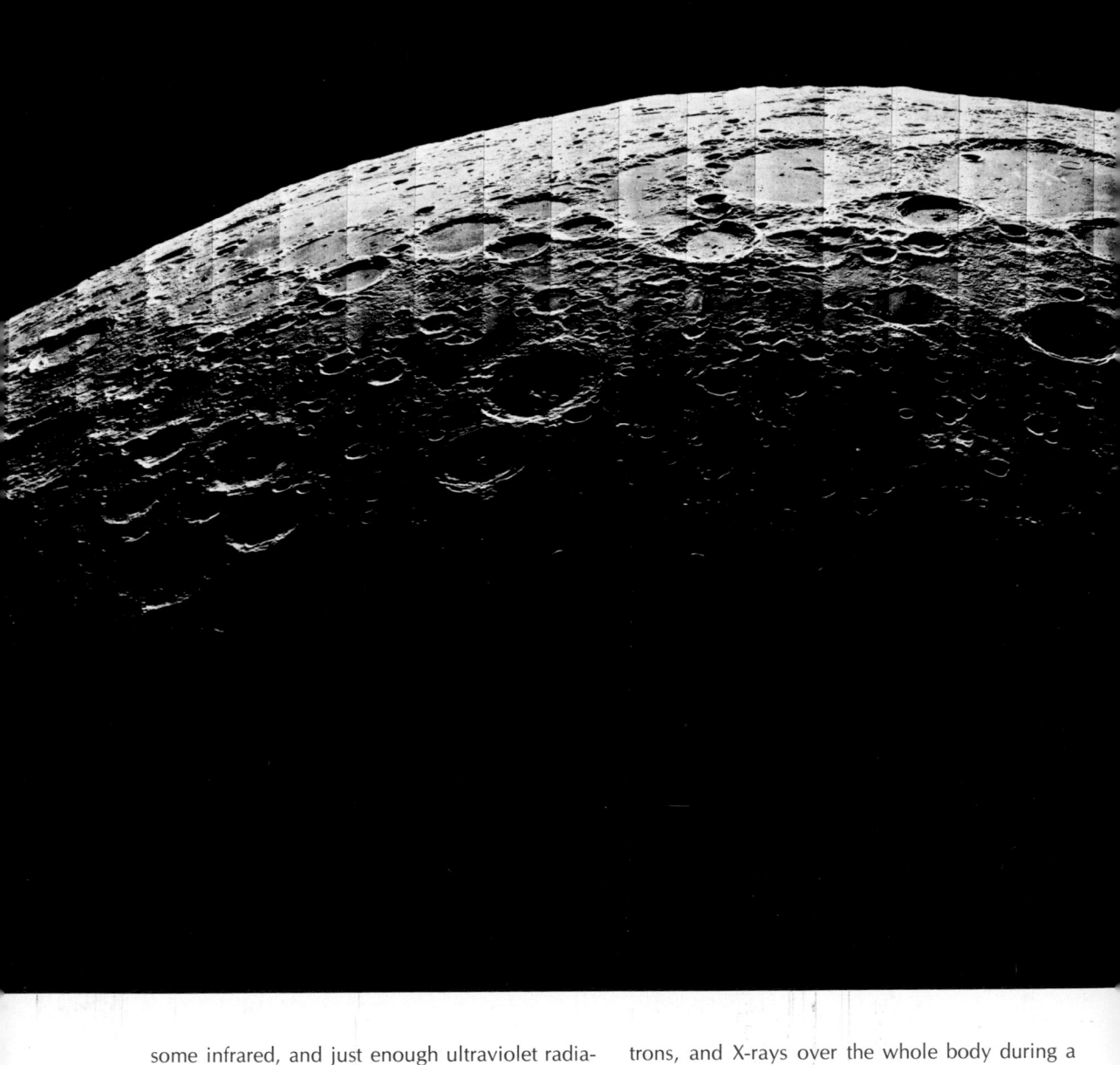

some infrared, and just enough ultraviolet radiation to cause sunburn.

At last we are safe, even from the awesome barrage of solar flare radiation.

Above the atmosphere, Conrad and Gordon in their craft and suits are safe too — except during a flare. Dangerous eruptions usually come weeks or months apart in more active periods on the sun, and occur rarely at other times. So far, weight limitations of rocket payloads have ruled out heavy metal shielding to guard against serious flares, unlikely to occur during short flights. But if the temperamental sun unexpectedly erupted, the men might be endangered.

While small doses of high-energy protons, elec-

trons, and X-rays over the whole body during a short time have no noticeable effect, heavy doses may cause vomiting within two hours. Enclosed in his space helmet, the astronaut could inhale the weightless, floating material and suffocate. If he escaped this danger, he might later develop some form of cancer from the radiation.

To avoid these threats, ground control would order the men to terminate the mission. On earth, radio listeners would notice crackling static as the solar storm hit the ionosphere. Near the poles, spectacular auroras would light the skies.

No unexpected solar flare troubled the flight of Gemini 11. Conrad, gazing out into the velvet-black backdrop of space, of course could see

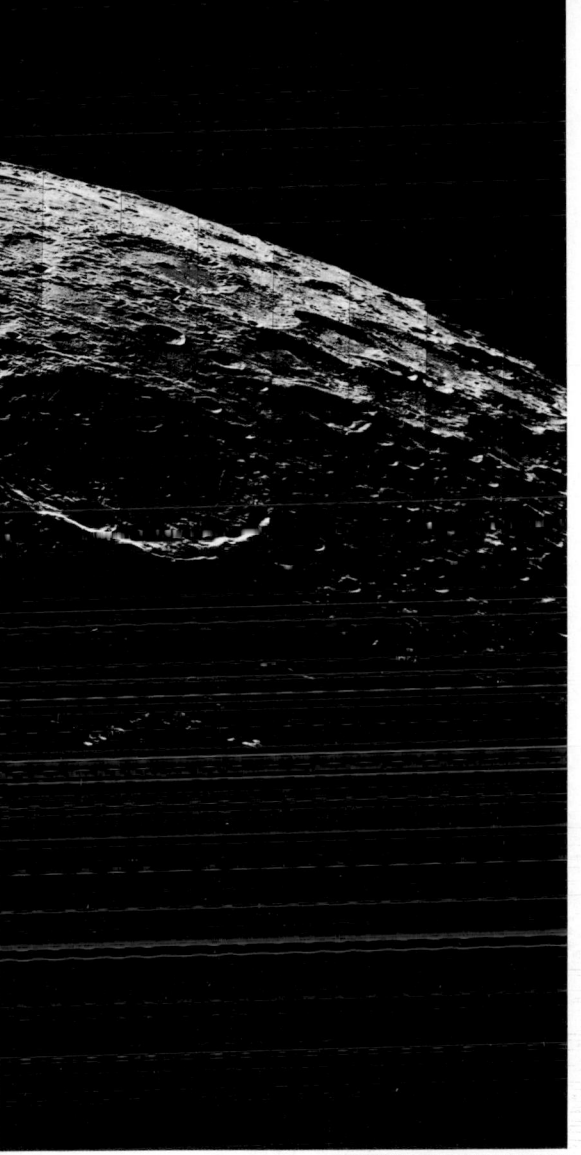

FAINT RAYS *of sunlight reveal a stark moonscape perpetually hidden from earthbound observers in this photograph taken by Lunar Orbiter V in 1967. Lacking the protective shield of earth and its atmosphere, this surface presents an easier target for meteorites and solar particles than does the earth side. Astrogeologist Eugene M. Shoemaker working in Flagstaff, Arizona, produces detailed maps of the moon's geologic and topographic structure from thousands of lunar photographs.*

nothing of the invisible, normal turbulence going on in the magnetosphere and atmosphere as rays, electrically charged particles, atoms, and molecules interacted. All he saw was smoke and smog hugging earth's surface in spots, some brush fires in Africa, clouds and lightning in the lower layers of air, and the airglow—an emission of faint green light from bands of oxygen atoms and a yellow light from bands of sodium atoms about 60 miles above the earth.

The astronauts took pictures of them all. They took pictures, too, of the sun, unobscured by our atmosphere as night changed into day along a definite line on the rotating earth. Like a distant fire in the night, only the sun's own disk is bright

while all about it remains black space. Only reflecting objects like earth and the Gemini 11 spacecraft and its companion, an orbiting Agena rocket, can catch the sun's light and be "lighted."

Perhaps the oddest aspect of space travel is weightlessness. Nothing has weight, not even the unpowered craft falling around earth in an orbit where its speed cancels out the pull of gravity. Inside the cabin everything floats unless fastened down. Conrad, tied to his seat, watched with fascination as "all the debris and junk . . . in the spacecraft went out the window" when Gordon opened it for his walk outside. "And I was right along with the rest of the debris," Dick said.

Floating idly was restful, but floating as he tried

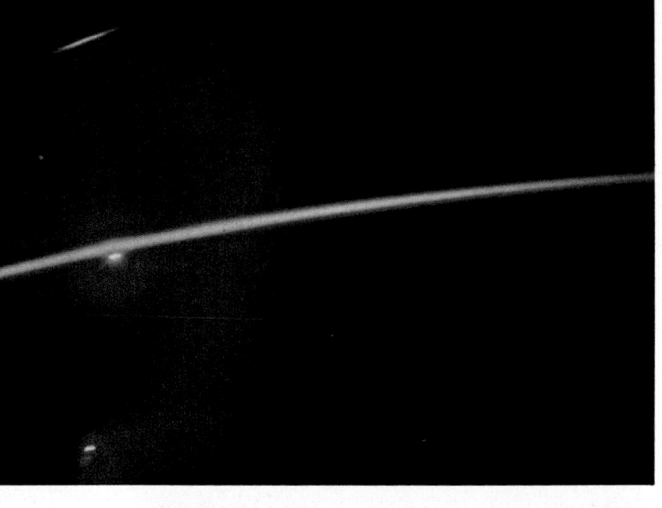

"**ORBITAL SUNSET** *is tremendous . . . a truly beautiful, beautiful sight,*" *reported Astronaut John Glenn during his 1962 flight in* Friendship 7. *Slipping below the horizon, the sun throws off its final golden rays and casts reflections on the capsule's window.*

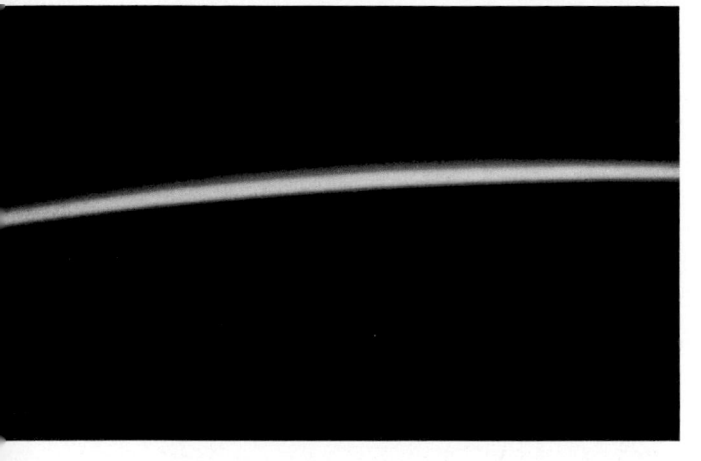

AFTER SETTING, *the sun leaves behind colorful bands of twilight caused by the scattering and refraction of light rays in the atmosphere. This thin, dense layer contains most of the air breathable by man.*

to work made Gordon sweat and gasp. His muscles had to force his arms to raise and keep his body in front of the craft as he tried to hook it by a tether to an Agena rocket. Finally, in desperation, he climbed astride the spacecraft and wedged his legs between it and the docking nose. "Ride 'em cowboy!" Conrad called to him by radio. Minutes later, Conrad eased the nose of his craft into the docking collar of Agena.

The astronauts found and docked with the rocket during their first orbit, a record for making a

rendezvous. Thrust into space at the precise second that would make the job easy, the men calculated their rocket-firing maneuvers with a compact computer and steered straight for the target. One firing put Gemini 11 into the same plane below Agena; a second brought the craft up to Agena's orbit, but ahead of the rocket; the third braked Gemini to let Agena close in.

Conrad and Gordon's performance was almost perfect. But if they had started the first "burn" of the thrusters even a second too early or too late, or let it go on too long or too little, the spacecraft would have missed by miles the exact point necessary for the success of the next burn. Errors could have been corrected by another succession of thrusts, braking to drop into a lower but speedier orbit in order to catch up with Agena or shooting upward to rise into the slower orbit of Agena. Additional burns, however, would have used up fuel intended for other jobs on the flight—jobs the astronauts might have had to cancel.

On the third day, the two astronauts had another unusual chance to experience orbital physics in action—even to worry about it—and to stick their heads into the bottom edge of the Van Allen belt. After locking the nose of their craft into the Agena, they fired its rocket, propelling themselves about 675 miles higher. A jolt of acceleration and the gravity it created interrupted their weightless state. "Whoop-de-doo!" laughed Conrad. "Look at it go!" They climbed so fast, in fact, that he later commented, ". . . we just had the impression that we were . . . going straight up. . . ." And Gordon added, "We were wondering if we were ever going to stop. . . ."

The new orbit attained an apogee, or high point, about 850 miles above earth. Its perigee, or low point, was 185 miles. The craft speeded up at the low end of the orbit to nearly 18,000 miles an hour—the greatest speed yet attained by man. At the high end, over the suburbs of Brisbane, Australia, it slowed to about 15,000 miles an hour. The longer sweep upward and the slower speed allowed the craft to "linger" a few minutes over Australia and the Pacific and Indian Oceans.

Enjoying an unprecedented view, Conrad shouted into his two-way radio, "It's utterly fantastic! I've got India in our left window and Borneo under our nose!" The astronauts made two of these lopsided flights before the Agena rocket shot them back to their former circular orbit.

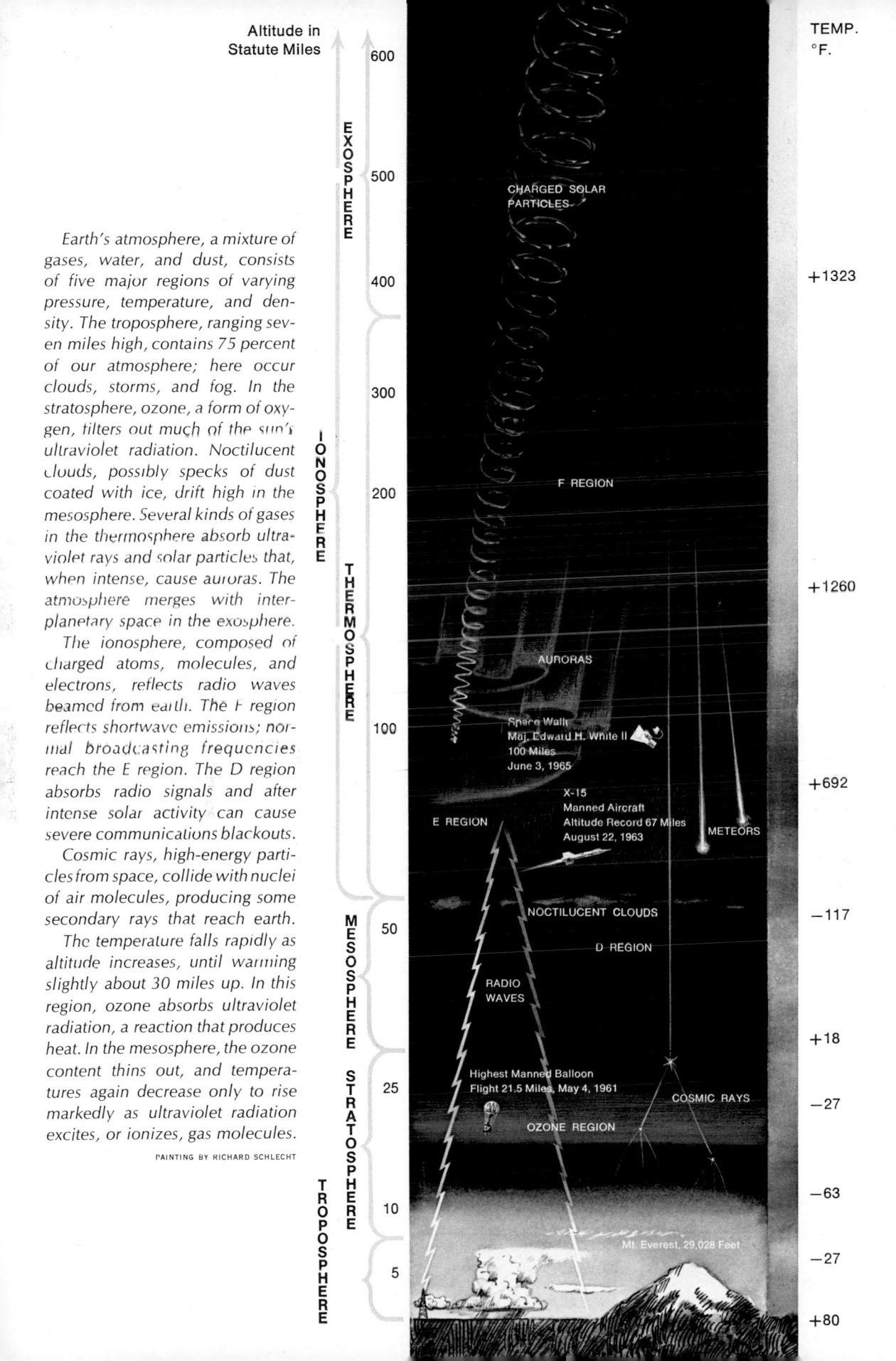

Altitude in
Statute Miles

TEMP.
°F.

Earth's atmosphere, a mixture of gases, water, and dust, consists of five major regions of varying pressure, temperature, and density. The troposphere, ranging seven miles high, contains 75 percent of our atmosphere; here occur clouds, storms, and fog. In the stratosphere, ozone, a form of oxygen, filters out much of the sun's ultraviolet radiation. Noctilucent clouds, possibly specks of dust coated with ice, drift high in the mesosphere. Several kinds of gases in the thermosphere absorb ultraviolet rays and solar particles that, when intense, cause auroras. The atmosphere merges with interplanetary space in the exosphere.

The ionosphere, composed of charged atoms, molecules, and electrons, reflects radio waves beamed from earth. The F region reflects shortwave emissions; normal broadcasting frequencies reach the E region. The D region absorbs radio signals and after intense solar activity can cause severe communications blackouts.

Cosmic rays, high-energy particles from space, collide with nuclei of air molecules, producing some secondary rays that reach earth.

The temperature falls rapidly as altitude increases, until warming slightly about 30 miles up. In this region, ozone absorbs ultraviolet radiation, a reaction that produces heat. In the mesosphere, the ozone content thins out, and temperatures again decrease only to rise markedly as ultraviolet radiation excites, or ionizes, gas molecules.

PAINTING BY RICHARD SCHLECHT

RICHARD SCHLECHT

SCARRING THE DAWN SKY *near Washington, D. C., the comet Ikeya-Seki (opposite) stretches its 75-million-mile tail starward during its 1965 sweep past the sun. The comet closed to within 300,000 miles of the solar surface, at speeds up to a million miles an hour. Composed of gases, porous solids, and ice, comets heat and luminesce as they approach the sun. The tail forms from cometary material swept back by the charged particles of the solar wind. This force exerts a pressure strong enough to push the tail away from the sun's surface (above). Below, Saxons point fearfully toward Halley's comet, which appeared in 1066, a few months before the Norman invasion of England. This 11th-century Bayeux Tapestry interprets the visitation as an evil omen. Visible on earth at intervals of 76 years, the comet will return during 1986.*

MILTON A. FORD AND VICTOR R. BOSWELL, JR., N.G.S. STAFF (BELOW), BY SPECIAL PERMISSION OF THE CITY OF BAYEUX; VICTOR R. BOSWELL, JR., (OPPOSITE)

At a high point on their first elliptical orbit, they had opened the hatch. Gordon stood up, his head and shoulders in space, his weightless tethered body floating a little above the floor. For two hours he took pictures of the earth—great reaches of oceans, whole mountain ranges, vast pink deserts, heavy green jungles—and the stars.

During two "night" periods of less than an hour each, the astronauts searched out the stars Antares and Canopus and the constellations Scorpio and Orion. The stars shone with a bright, steady light. The twinkle caused by earth's busy, shimmering atmosphere no longer blurred their outlines. Conrad turned the craft to the best position and Gordon aimed their specially designed camera to catch ultraviolet rays emitted in vast quantities from the young hot stars.

During a short lull in their picture-taking, both unexpectedly dropped off to sleep, Gordon with his head still out the hatch! Why not? there was no noise to bother them; without air, space is completely silent except for radio voices piped inside the helmet. Conrad woke first from his catnap and called to his companion. "Huh? Oh . . ." said Gordon and aimed the camera again.

He had been scheduled to get pictures of two faint clouds of moondust—if they exist—one preceding, one trailing the moon in its orbit. Scientists believe that dust escapes into space when meteoroids hit the surface of the low-gravity moon. Two neutral pockets created by an overlap in the fields of gravity of the earth and the moon trap some of the dust before it is pulled to earth. "Little parts of the moon are falling on us all the time," says Dr. Eugene M. Shoemaker, chief scientist at the U. S. Geological Survey's Center of Astrogeology in Flagstaff, Arizona. But the glare of the Milky Way prevented Dick from seeing the pockets, and the mystery of the dusty clouds remains.

Speeding dust, somewhat larger grains of matter, and even pellets from various celestial sources rush through the space around earth. In the regions where the astronauts were orbiting, they could expect to hear an occasional tiny ping when a speck of matter about half the size of a grain of sand struck their craft. "Astronauts who have heard the impacts say they sound like bird shot pellets on a tin roof," says Astrophysicist Curtis L. Hemenway, director of Dudley Observatory, Albany, N.Y. Sample squares of material that Dr. Hemenway arranged in boxes attached to long-

orbiting satellites have recorded the dents left by impacting micrometeoroids.

An international group of experts has agreed, Dr. Hemenway says, that the impact rate is about one micrometeoroid every hundred seconds on a surface of about one yard square. For a craft the size of Gemini 11, that would amount to about a million pieces of microscopic dust a month and perhaps a hundred barely visible particles. The chances that during a month a craft would be struck, perhaps pierced, by a meteoroid as big as a garden pea are about one in a million.

When a meteoroid reaches earth's atmosphere, it may be traveling as much as a hundred thousand miles an hour. Superheated air in the shock wave it creates burns the meteoroid—now a shooting star—just as it would burn Conrad and Gordon's craft if it had no heat shield when it re-entered earth's atmosphere. Particles of microscopic

dust, on the other hand, like tiny parachutes, slow down and float gently to the ground. About a thousand tons of dust fall on us every day, judging from the evidence collected by spacecraft.

Out of the open hatch, the astronauts could see Venus and Mars, our nearest planetary neighbors. Beyond Mars where the next planet logically should be lies the asteroid belt. There great chunks of rock fly around the sun. At least 50,000 of them have been detected, ranging in size from mile-wide rocks to spheres and irregular lumps up to 470 miles across. Occasionally, one escapes its orbit and falls to earth as a meteorite. Some authorities believe that asteroids are fragments of an exploded planet. Others think that Jupiter's gravitational force may have prevented a single large planet from forming. And perhaps small planets developed, then collided and shattered.

If astronauts ever attempt a flight to Jupiter, they

will have to dodge the huge fragments in the asteroid belt. Other space debris, perhaps left by comets, might cause future astronauts a problem too.

About 870 known comets journey around the sun, usually in extremely elliptical paths coming close to the sun at one end, and swinging far beyond the edge of the solar system at the other. Their enormous cloudy heads measure up to several hundred thousands of miles across. Scientists believe that in many comets, this "cloud" surrounds a ball of rock- and dust-filled, frozen gases sometimes 50 miles in diameter. Near the sun, some of the gases in the "snowball" thaw and cause the cloud around it to spread out spectacularly.

A tail forms when the solar wind particles and solar radiation pressure strike the cloud. The tail, as much as 100 million miles long, gradually disappears as the comet moves far away from the sun. Most astronomers think small meteoroids and mi-

crometeoroids are debris scattered along the comet's path. When the earth crosses that path, some debris plunges into our atmosphere and the night sky blazes with a flurry of shooting stars.

Conrad and Gordon carried out their observations, picture-taking, and instrument reading in space for scientists eager to have more definite information concerning the universe than they can ever hope to get on earth. A myriad of questions remains about what is out there and what is going on. Perhaps the most intriguing question to man is that of *who* is out there—if anybody.

Pete would probably take off tomorrow to look for the answers if there were a craft ready to go. He is the sort of man whose curiosity and sense of adventure would urge him on to get a close look at a planet, at a star, at another galaxy.

But the rockets available to him now wouldn't get him far. Our most powerful, the Saturn V, with

SOL GOLDBERG, CORNELL UNIVERSITY

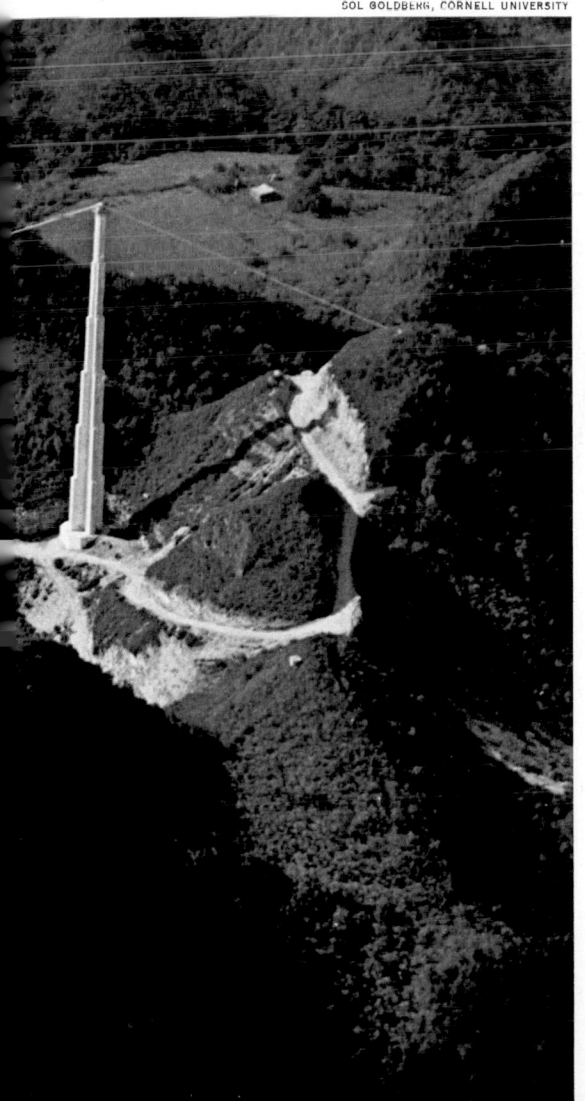

COMMONWEALTH OF PUERTO RICO

GIANT TELESCOPIC EAR, *the 1,000-foot-wide Arecibo Ionospheric Observatory in Puerto Rico explores the universe by sending and receiving radio waves. With radar, the station maps the surfaces of Mercury, Venus, and Mars and the earth's ionosphere. It also detects precisely timed bursts of radio energy, called pulsars, trillions of miles away. Capturing such waves, the wire-mesh bowl focuses them on the suspended antenna. Crossing the dish, a technician wears water skis to distribute his weight.*

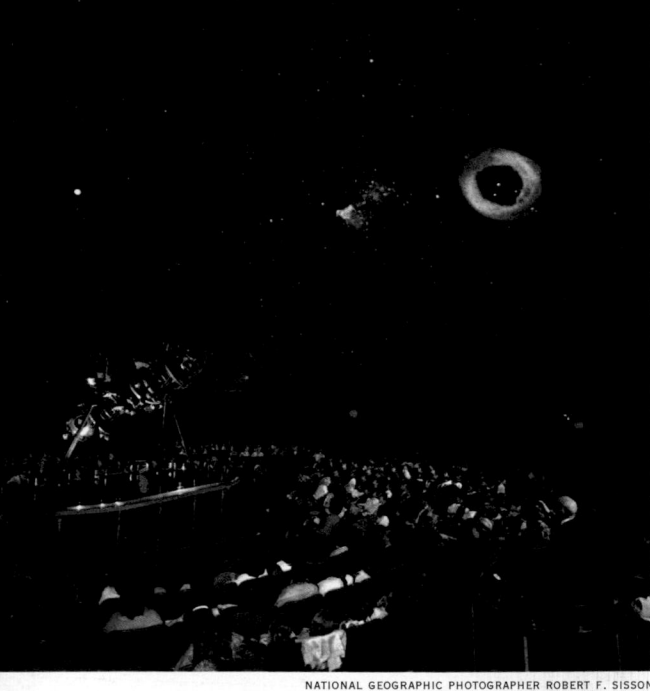

ANDROMEDA (opposite), sister of our Milky Way and one of billions of galaxies in the universe, whirls in space nearly three million light-years away. The hub glows yellow with ancient stellar giants; young blue stars shine among the spiral arms. Two smaller galaxies hover nearby. In the Hayden Planetarium in New York City (above), visitors view images of the universe on a domed ceiling. The Ring Nebula blazes above the projector.

7.5 million pounds of thrust, could take 140 tons of payload into orbit 120 miles high. Several such payloads, assembled in orbit into a nuclear-powered rocket, could go to Venus and Mars and return within two years. But to go farther and return is beyond even the Nerva nuclear engine now being developed, since it requires bulky supplies of liquid hydrogen, which is heated by the reactor to produce a high-velocity exhaust gas.

Two new types of engine, now used in experimental flights in both the U. S. and Russia, provide exhaust thrust with beams of highly accelerated mercury or cesium ions and electrons. These engines require stores of fuel small enough to be practical for long journeys once underway. The thrust of each engine is small, but it can build up high speeds for craft in frictionless space.

In the ion engine, beams of positive ions ac-celerated by an electric field exhaust from the rear of the engine as they mix with a stream of negative electrons. On a similar principle, the plasma engine uses electromagnetic forces to accelerate both ions and electrons into an exhaust beam.

Both rockets require great quantities of electricity, however, and the speeds they achieve would be far below the speed of light, 186,000 miles a second.

The distance even to the nearest star, around which hospitable planets may or may not be orbiting, is measured in light-years, the distance light travels in a year—about six trillion miles. Obviously, if man wants to go into stellar space, he must travel as close to the speed of light as he can or else he will never be able to make the trip out and back in a lifetime. According to Einstein, the velocity of light is the ultimate speed limit, never to be exceeded. Man could never really hope to go that fast, he said.

But perhaps man can travel almost that fast, some dreamers think, and they suggest the photon rocket as a likely means. Scientists know that light and other electromagnetic rays exert pressure when they strike a surface. Even now some scientists suggest that astronauts on journeys to Venus or Mars could unfurl enormous light-reflecting sails, catch the pressure of light from the sun, and eventually travel at high velocities without using any fuel! The pressure produced by powerful beams of photons shooting from a rocket might succeed in accelerating the craft to velocities approaching the speed of light—or radio waves.

But would Pete like going 6,000 trillion miles to some distant star if, according to the different time scale Einstein said would prevail during his trip, he came back only three decades older to find that the earth had aged more than 2,000 years! As Dr. Wernher von Braun says, "He might wind up in a zoo."

No thanks, Pete might understandably reply. Then again, he might repeat the remark he made soon after returning from the flight of Gemini 11: "Give me a good night's sleep, and I'm ready to go back again."

Whether Pete Conrad, or another astronaut, exceeds the 850-mile penetration of space, his trip and his data will take us one step closer to picking up a piece of the moon or Mars—or a handful of stardust. And it will make one more significant contribution to man's knowledge of his universe.

Great Nebula, a vast cloud of dust scattering stellar light
and gas fluorescing under the stimulus of hot stars nearby, glows
brilliantly in the constellation Orion. Some 1,500 light
years from earth, this brightest-looking of all the Milky Way's
nebulae appears near the middle of Orion's sword.

4/ THE ALIEN ENVIRONMENT: MAN LEARNS TO ADJUST

With a single exception, the 30 men who rocketed skyward during the first six years of manned space exploration experienced a sense of freedom and exhilaration as they escaped the bonds of gravity and began weightless flight. Only Gherman Titov—the world's fourth space man, after Gagarin, Shepard, and Grissom—reported an adverse physical reaction in attempting to adapt to the new environment.

Of his experience on entering orbit the morning of August 6, 1961, Titov wrote: "For the life of me I could not determine where I was . . . I felt suddenly as though I were turning a somersault and then flying with my legs up! . . . I was completely confused, unable to define where was earth or the stars. It seemed as if the somersault had carried me completely around and that I was floating upside down, attached to nothing . . . everything whirled around in a strange fog that defied all attempts to separate order from the sudden chaos. Something had gone suddenly and drastically wrong with . . . my sense of balance. My sense of orientation vanished abruptly and completely."

Although Titov's disorientation lasted only seconds, he later developed dizziness and nausea that remained with him during most of his 17-orbit mission. His experience caused such widespread concern that for a time after his flight, some experts in bioastronautics questioned whether man could function for prolonged periods in space.

But Titov's reaction proved to be a purely personal one, much as some people suffer from vertigo or seasickness. He had performed normally in preflight training, and physicians had no inkling that he would respond as he did in space.

It is remarkable indeed that man has encountered so little physical difficulty on his first ventures into the alien environment overhead. The father of the communications satellite, space scientist and writer Arthur C. Clarke, once expressed the implication of space flight in a vivid analogy: Man's entry into space, he suggested, could be compared to life's original entry into the

WILD RIDE *in a bizarre experimental chair tests a pilot's ability to stabilize his space capsule as it hurtles into the lower atmosphere. A control stick counters roll, pitch, and yaw. Engineers at the Lewis Research Center in Cleveland, Ohio, attached lights to the frame to trace the tumbling.*

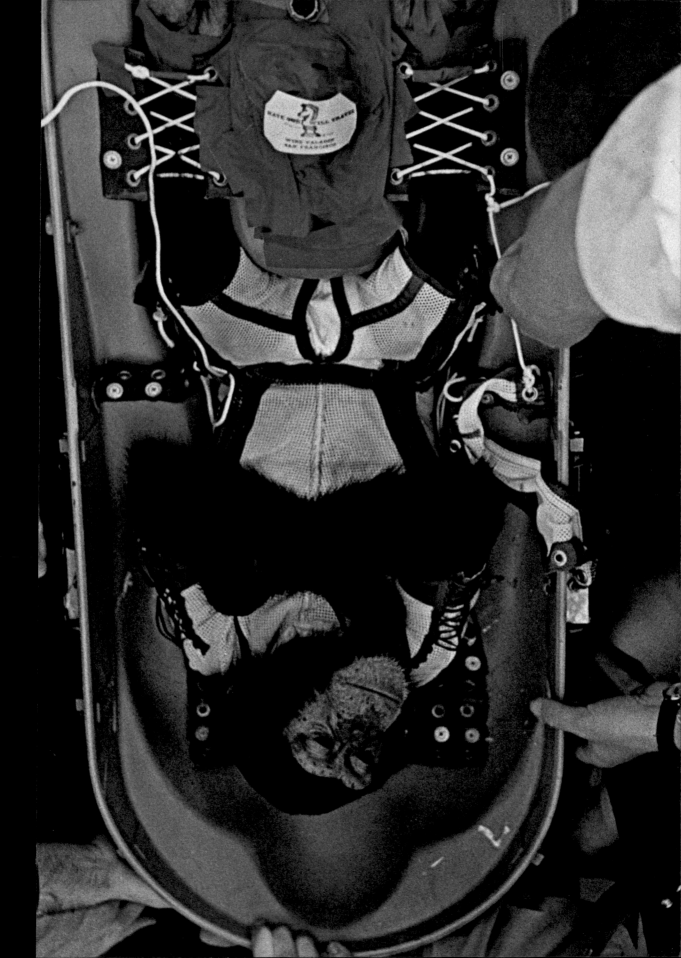

new and formidable province of land and air. In his book, *Voices from the Sky,* he noted: Life left the sea despite the fact that it composed what he called "the perfect environment for life."

"In the sea," Clarke wrote, "an all pervading fluid medium carries oxygen and food directly to each organism. The same medium neutralizes gravity, insures against temperature extremes, and prevents damage by too intense solar radiation, which must have been lethal at the earth's surface before the ozone layer was formed.

"It seems incredible that life ever left the sea because in some ways dry land is almost as dangerous as space. . . . We seldom stop to think that we are still creatures of the sea, able to leave it only because, from birth to death, we wear the water-filled space suits of our skins."

As Clarke's comparison implies, we must make complex adjustments to new hazards before we can truly explore the realm of space.

Man's knowledge of space hazards dates only from the mid-17th century. Until that time, most people believed that the air we breathe extended all the way to the moon. Man himself, they thought, could just go on wearing his normal attire as he worked, ate, and slept his way through space.

Lucian of Samosata, a fantasy writer who lived some 1,800 years ago, sent his passengers to the moon on a ship powered by winds. It was Johannes Kepler's fictional account of a moon trip about 1630 that first suggested lack of air and gravity in space, anticipating by 60 years Isaac Newton's formulation of the laws of gravity.

High-altitude balloon experiments, beginning about 1800, placed the first deposits in the bank of man's knowledge of the lethal cold and lack of oxygen awaiting the space traveler. Balloon flights dramatically underscored the fact that the breathable atmosphere, far from extending into space, is

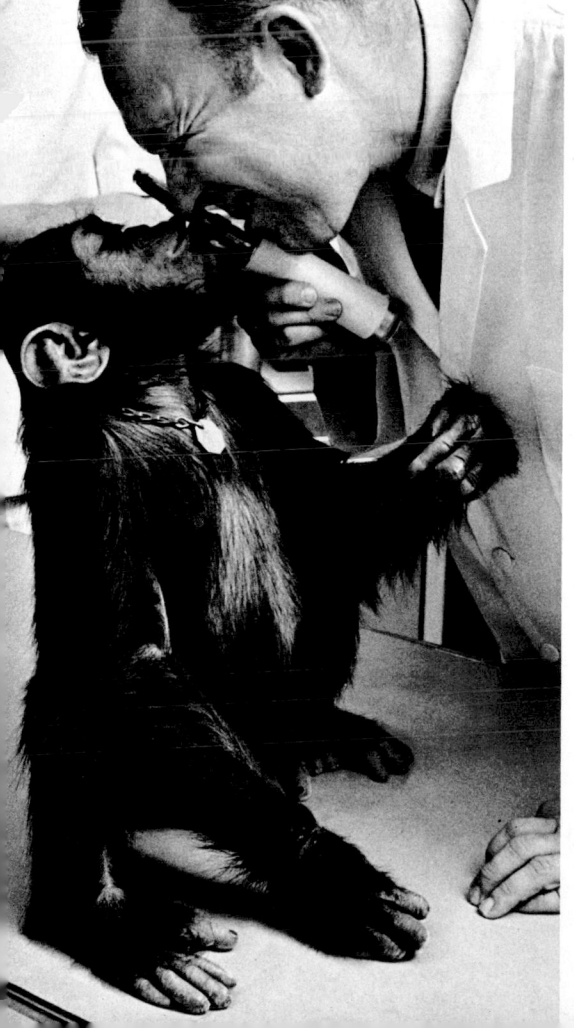

FRECKLED CHIMP HAM, *a forerunner of man in space, awaits release from his couch after a 16-minute, 5,800-mph flight in a Project Mercury capsule in 1961. Fired aloft by a Redstone rocket, Ham soared 156 miles high and splashed down in the Atlantic 414 miles from his launching pad at Cape Canaveral. Nuzzling a doctor, astrochimp candidate Billy sits for an eye examination. The Russian dog Laika, first animal to orbit the earth, died aboard Sputnik II in 1957 after remote sensors monitored her pulse, respiration, and other responses.*

HENRY BURROUGHS, ASSOCIATED PRESS, NASA (FAR LEFT);
NOVOSTI (TOP); RALPH CRANE, LIFE

compressed around the earth. In 1804 Frenchman L. J. Gay-Lussac recorded subzero temperatures at 23,000 feet, and in 1862 James Glaisher of England blacked out at 29,000 feet.

A few years later, two French balloonists died of oxygen starvation at 27,950 feet, the first casualties of high-altitude flight. To protect the body, Auguste Piccard of Switzerland designed a hermetically sealed balloon-cabin and in 1931 rose safely to nearly 52,000 feet.

In the age of flight, man overcame the hazards. He wore warm clothing; he donned an oxygen mask. Eventually, he created his own comfortable atmosphere by pressurizing his aircraft.

But since his planes could ascend only a few miles into the atmosphere, he could learn little of what lay beyond. For this he had to await the development of rockets capable of lifting him 30 miles or more. The attempt to send a man skyward by rocket occurred much earlier, however.

In the 1830's, Claude Ruggieri, former fireworks master for King Louis XVI of France, pro-posed to send a small boy up in a rocket he devised. Although Ruggieri had succeeded in launching mice and rats, the Paris police forbade his bold experiment with a human being. In any case, Ruggieri's simple parachute-equipped gunpowder rocket would not have taken a passenger anywhere near the limits of the breathable atmosphere.

The use of liquid-fuel rockets for biomedical experiments in space began after the U. S. gained possession of the German V-2's. Although the Nation's program eventually employed chimpanzees, university and military scientists first sent into space such varied specimens as fruit flies, seeds, yeast, sea-urchin eggs, onions, mice, and monkeys.

The program in the Soviet Union began in the 1940's and 1950's with white mice, frogs—even goldfish. But the Russians came to rely primarily on dogs for experimentation. While in Moscow in 1966, I asked one of the Soviet Union's leading experts in bioastronautics, Academician Vasili V. Parin, why this was so.

"The Russian dog," the gray-haired biologist

WHIRLPOOL CORPORATION (BELOW); NATIONAL GEOGRAPHIC PHOTOGRAPHER JAMES P. BLAIR (CENTER)

replied, "has always been a great friend of science. You know, of course, of the work of our famous psychologist, Ivan Pavlov, who studied the reflexes of dogs. But did you know that near Leningrad there is a monument in honor of Pavlov's dogs? We have amassed much data on our four-footed friends. Their circulation and respiration are close to that of man's. And they are very patient and durable under long experiments."

Prior to Laika's epic flight, Soviet scientists worked out life-support systems for dogs launched straight up by rocket, eventually sending a two-dog capsule to an altitude of 279 miles.

When the Russians decided to send Laika into orbit, they made no provision for bringing her back. Their main goals were to discover how life reacted to extended weightlessness and to improve flight-safety systems. They felt that if they could keep the dog alive for a week and monitor her responses, they could obtain the data they needed.

To provide a breathing mixture, they installed a container of oxygen and a regenerator to cleanse the air of exhaled carbon dioxide and water vapor. For nourishment, Laika would consume food suspended in gelatin. Body wastes would be contained in a rubber reservoir attached to her pelvic area.

Electrodes and sensors would monitor Laika's pulse, respiration rates, and movement; tiny radio transmitters would broadcast the data to earth.

The mission went as planned. Before Laika died, she demonstrated that living organisms could adapt to space flight.

"Laika's flight," Soviet scientist Aleksei Ivanov wrote later, "made it possible to speak more boldly and concretely of the possibility of cosmic journeys of men."

In the meantime, the United States was approaching the same conclusion by somewhat different means. On May 28, 1959, two monkeys, Able and Baker, soared aloft from Cape Canaveral,

SQUEEZED FROM A TUBE, *reconstituted orange juice nourishes a space-suited technician in a test of the Gemini menu. While in orbit, astronauts received 2,500 calories daily. Plastic containers keep the food from floating away during meals in space. Injected into a sack (below), water rehydrates a freeze-dried meal equal to a full-course dinner. Astronaut Alan Bean (right) chews on boa constrictor during a jungle-survival course in Panama.*

reaching an altitude of 300 miles, a speed of 10,000 miles per hour, and traveling a distance of 1,071 miles downrange. After their safe return, scientists proceeded with plans for the eventual launching and recovery of chimpanzees.

One such flight in 1961, that of a remarkably stable ape named Enos, went a long way toward proving that a chimp is more humanlike in space than a dog. At intervals during his two-orbit flight, colored lights flashed. If Enos then alertly pressed a lever, as he was trained to do, he could obtain banana pellets and water—and avoid mild electric shocks. The action of pressing the lever signaled ground stations that he was purposefully performing his duty while in weightless flight.

But trouble developed in the circuitry, and even though America's first orbiter was prompt in pressing the lever he often got a shock anyway. Later, in-flight photographs showed Enos baring his teeth in exasperation; nevertheless, he continued to press the lever every time the light flashed.

I saw Enos at a press conference just after his recovery. The astrochimp struck me as poised and alert. Remarkably, he still relished banana pellets.

Enos's performance may have inspired a cartoon I have often seen in the Houston home of my neighbor, John Glenn, where it hangs framed on a wall. The drawing shows a cocksure chimpanzee pointing to a blackboard medical chart as he briefs a row of attentive astronauts.

"And at about this point," he is telling them, "you get an overwhelming desire for a banana."

Now, at last, man had reached the point of launching himself into space. Ages earlier, life had only one way to survive when it left the sea: adapt, through evolution, to such unaccustomed factors as gravity, air, and radiation. Life today, however —in the form of intelligent, impatient, inventive *Homo sapiens*—can construct devices capable of insulating itself from the alien environment. Man can pack everything he needs into a life-sustaining "box," where he can live and work in space for as long as required.

This is essentially what the U.S.S.R. and the United States did when they built their earliest spacecraft—Vostok and Mercury. Their scientists and engineers had to construct capsules that would withstand severe subzero cold, extreme heat, and the brutal stresses of launch, re-entry, and landing.

When I saw the spherical Vostok in Russia, I noticed a metal shell that appeared to be nearly

CHOCO INDIAN of Panama watches astronaut-in-training Walter Cunningham dine on spit-roasted iguana. During a 1963 survival course, John Glenn

EDWARD HARRISON, NASA

(lower left) prepared for the possibility of coming down in jungle—rather than at sea as planned. On a Nevada desert, Michael Collins, with ma-

chete, and Charles A. Bassett II pitch parachute tents against the heat. In Panama, a length of bamboo stores water for Astronaut Richard Gordon.

N.G.S. PHOTOGRAPHER OTIS IMBODEN (ABOVE); ARI UHLMAN, NASA (CENTER); BILL TAUB, NASA (RIGHT)

WILLIAM ALBERT ALLARD (ABOVE); RALPH MORSE, LIFE, NASA

two inches thick. Except for hatches and glass ports, the craft seemed as solid as the boiler of a locomotive. Mercury used a thin outer shell of cobalt-nickel shingles, an inch and a half of insulation, and an inner shell of corrugated titanium.

Additionally, engineers had to create and sustain a livable atmosphere, both in the craft and in the spacemen's pressure suits. The Russians chose a basic nitrogen-oxygen mixture much like the air we breathe on earth. The United States decided to use pure oxygen. Air-conditioning systems would control temperatures inside the capsule.

The remarkable thing about both Vostok and Mercury was that they worked astonishingly well —and their pilots reacted to space flight with enthusiasm. "I could easily become a zero-g addict," John Glenn admitted. "Vostok 1," Gagarin said in a moment of exuberance, was "more beautiful

than a locomotive, a steamer, a plane, a palace, and a bridge—more beautiful than all of these creations put together."

Space pilots of both countries functioned so superbly that they helped dissolve many early fears that the human machine was not sturdy enough for space travel. A number of biologists and physicians had believed that man could not adapt to weightlessness. They feared that muscles might atrophy if relieved of the stress of gravity for long periods. Whether an astronaut sits or stands in space during weightless flight makes no difference—his muscles remain in a relaxed, or "floating," position.

Other experts predicted that either high or low blood pressure would result when the heart was suddenly freed of its normal task of supplying blood to the brain by pumping against gravity.

SUBMERGED FOR HOURS, *a test subject lies in a tank simulating the long periods of weightlessness that moon-bound astronauts will experience. A scientist at the Aerospace Medical Division, Brooks Air Force Base, Texas, observes his reaction. Tubes carry food as well as air. Below, astronauts experience zero-g's for just under half a minute as their KC-135 jet tanker arcs over the roller-coaster crest of a parabolic curve. Captain Bassett floats above Maj. Edwin E. Aldrin, Jr., and Capt. Theodore C. Freeman. Their instructor hugs the padded cabin wall. Plane crashes later took the lives of both Bassett and Freeman.*

And the gravity-sensitive inner ear caused concern. It is this delicate mechanism that enables us to detect motion and acceleration, and to keep our balance. Would the weightless state confuse it, doctors wondered, and deprive an astronaut of his sense of orientation?

As such fears were put aside, the second phase of manned flight—the U. S. Project Gemini and the Soviet Voskhod 1 and 2 of the mid-1960's—received more ambitious biomedical assignments. In Voskhod 1, cosmonaut-physiologist Boris Yegorov had with him a medical investigation kit. He took blood samples and measured the blood pressure of other Voskhod crewmen—the senior engineer pilot, Vladimir Komarov, and a civilian scientist, Konstantin Feoktistov. His instruments recorded brain waves, took electrocardiograms, and tested muscular coordination.

Space-walk experiments showed that man could leave his craft, protected only by a specially designed suit, either to make repairs or to explore the lunar surface.

The length of the space trips during the series of ten manned Gemini flights seemed to make little difference to the astronauts physically. Flights ranging in duration from five hours to 14 days produced similar reactions. "In general," said Dr. Charles A. Berry, Director of Medical Research and Operations at the Manned Spacecraft Center at Houston, Texas, "the environmental hazards and the effects on man appear to be of less magnitude than originally anticipated."

Some body changes did occur—bone density lessened slightly, minute quantities of calcium and protein nitrogen were lost, the blood's red cell count dropped by 5 to 20 percent, and the heart

was "lazy" for a time after its vacation in space.

Blood pressure, however, remained within normal ranges, no muscular atrophy or loss of coordination occurred, and even the two-week flight caused no motion sickness or disorientation. The bodies of the astronauts have all adapted rapidly to the multiple stresses of space flight—stresses that include confinement, the restraint of pressure suits, 100 percent oxygen atmosphere, acceleration forces, weightlessness, vibration, dehydration, altered work-sleep cycles, tension, and a demanding workload.

Of all the stresses, least was known about weightlessness; the part it played in causing or accentuating physical changes has yet to be fully assessed. Whatever the causes, the body changes disappeared after a day or two back on earth.

A more normal spacecraft atmosphere, more comfortable clothing, exercise equipment, and perhaps a measure of artificial gravity may reduce many of the problems of stress, but the only way to determine with certainty the effects of extended weightlessness is through longer and longer space flights. During 1969, the United States plans to send monkeys into orbit for a month to monitor their reactions. In the 1970's U. S. space stations may house men in the weightless state for a year or more—time enough to assess their capacity for a possible flight to Venus and back.

One whose opinion I sought on man's capacity for space flight was Dr. Oleg Gazenko who, along with Academician Parin, was an early leader in the Soviet bioastronautics program. I found him in Moscow in a former palace of Czar Nicholas I, which now houses the Soviet Academy of Sciences. Dr. Gazenko is an extremely polite, highly intense man of about 38. I asked him if he were optimistic about man's ability to make sustained flights in space. He pulled at his mustache and thought for a long moment.

"If you mean by sustained flight, a flight to the moon and back," he finally replied, "then I am

CREW-CUT ASTRONAUT *M. Scott Carpenter walks a straight line, evidencing unimpaired equilibrium after his 1962 three-orbit mission in Project Mercury's* Aurora 7. *Below, electrodes attached to Walter M. Schirra, Jr., record the physical effects of a six-orbit flight in* Sigma 7 *the same year.*

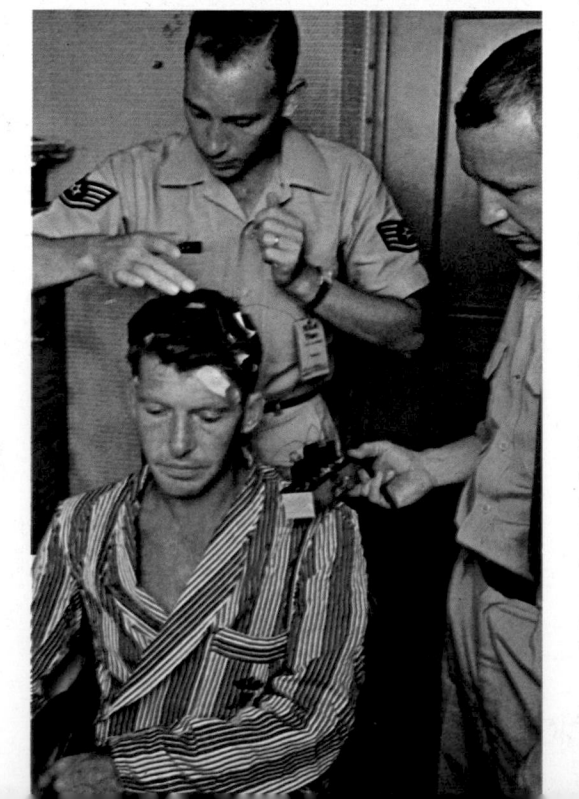

BACK FROM ORBIT *after a record-breaking 14 days aboard Gemini 7, James A. Lovell, Jr., rubs a growth of beard, and fellow Astronaut Frank Borman waves to photographers waiting aboard the recovery carrier U.S.S.* Wasp. *In a space rendezvous on December 15, 1965, three days before the pair splashed down in the Atlantic, another twin-seater,* Gemini 6, *maneuvered to within a foot of them.*

NATIONAL GEOGRAPHIC PHOTOGRAPHER DEAN CONGER (ABOVE); BILL TAUB, NASA (LEFT); LEE JONES, NASA

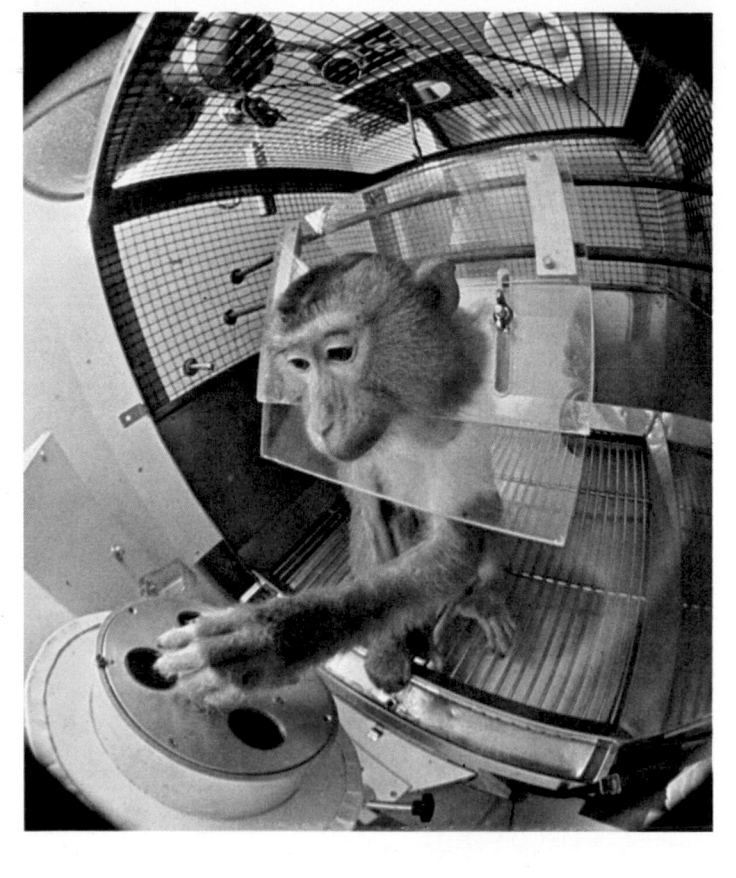

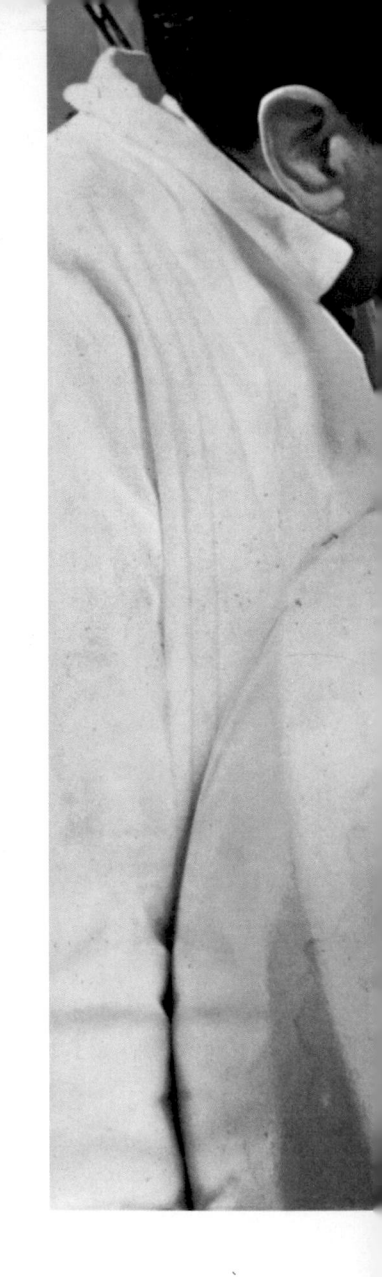

PUNCHING LIGHTS *in sequence, a pigtail monkey practices a task it will do in a biological research capsule scheduled to orbit the earth in 1969. At right, scientists at the Biosatellite Laboratory of the University of California at Los Angeles watch the primate operate a lever on a feeding machine. The animal's skullcap contains electrodes that will record brain and muscle reactions. Below, the smaller-eyed* Habrobracon *wasp—second-generation offspring of an insect that survived a 1967 space flight—shows mutations in the size of its eyes and the color of its body in comparison with a normal wasp.*

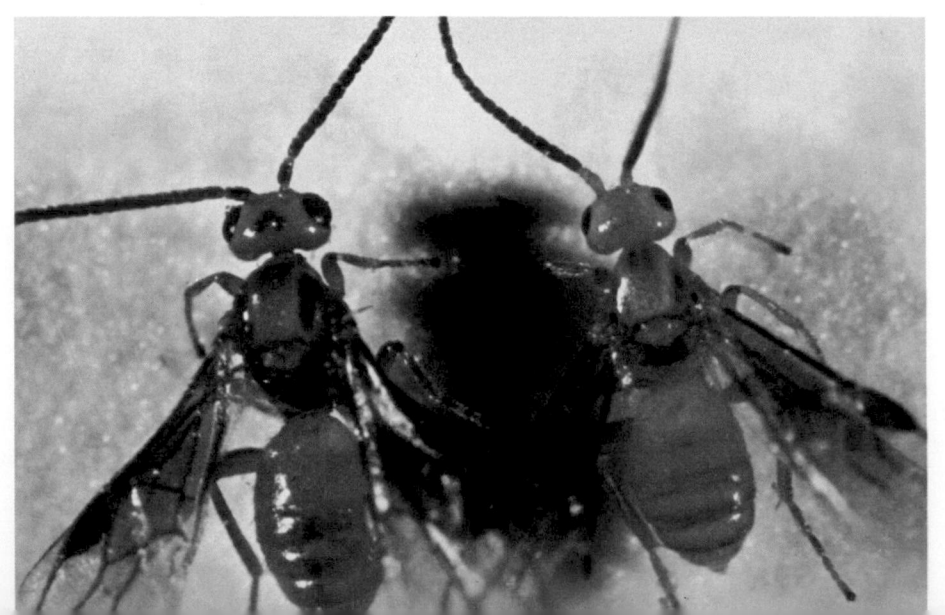

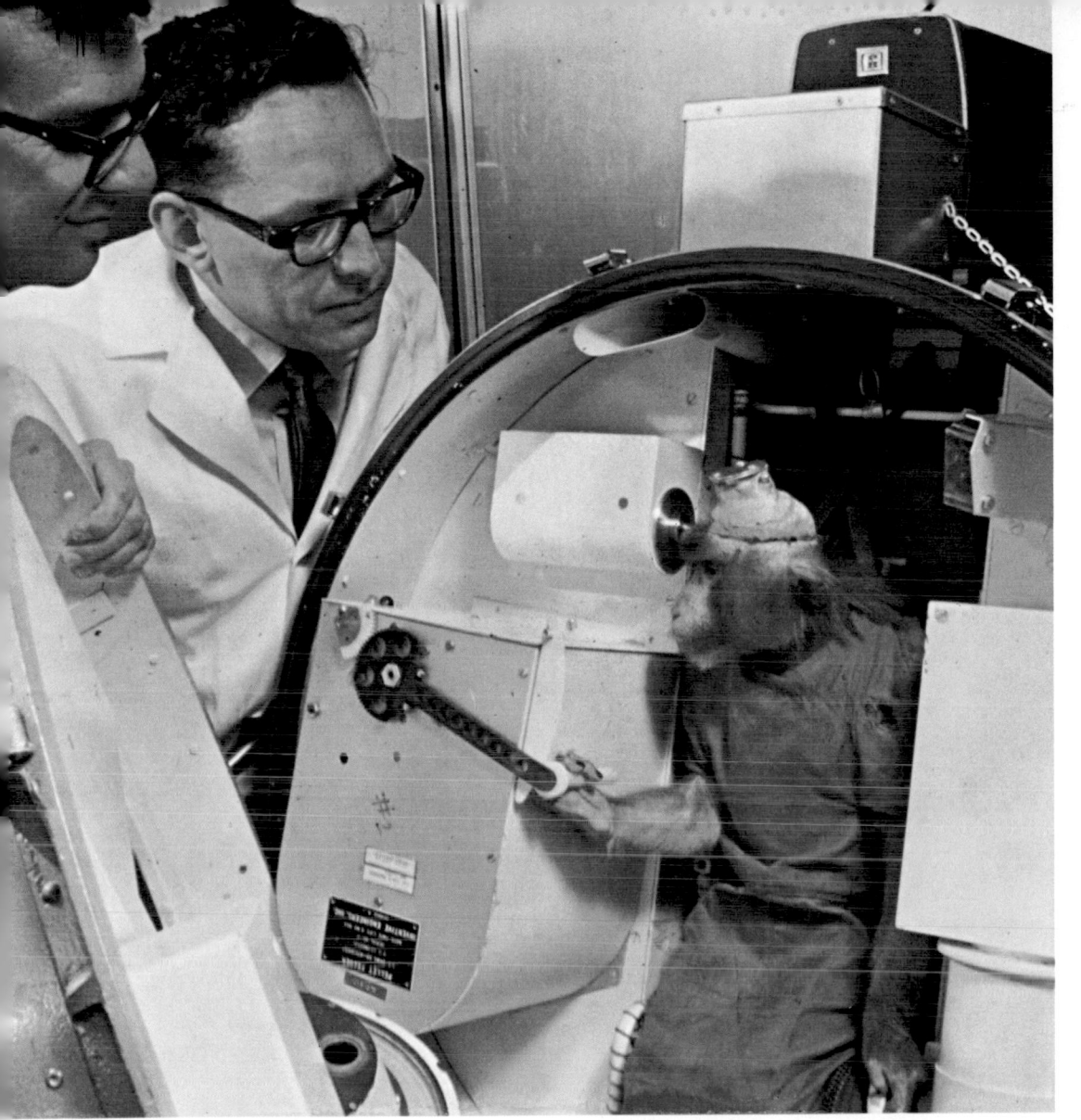

optimistic. But if you mean a flight to Mars or Venus requiring several months then I must express caution. There are so many unknowns. What we have found so far is a combination of facts affecting man in space that in many ways puzzles us. Before we can be optimistic, we must make better use of the facts we already have. And we must have more facts."

As man prepares for lunar exploration, one thing appears clear. Space physicians of both East and West agree that flying to the moon should present no insurmountable medical obstacles. To the surprise of many people, ionizing radiation—such as X-rays—has posed little problem thus far in orbital flights. The walls of the craft have provided an adequate shield. During flights to the moon,

the vehicle will go through the Van Allen belt rapidly, making further shielding unnecessary.

On the moon, authorities say, the normal weekly radiation level is about the equivalent of a chest X-ray, but with the exposure distributed over the whole body. Astronauts should suffer no adverse effects during stays free of solar flares. The space suit itself will protect man from ultraviolet rays.

In times of solar eruptions, however, when the sun hurls out its greatly increased flow of ionizing particles, spacemen walking on the moon would face a major hazard. But ideally such flares will be detected far enough in advance to give the moon explorers ample time to return to the added protection of their space ship.

Thus far, man has had one dependable constant

that has provided him with both a directional reference and a psychological anchor — his knowledge that he can see mother earth just outside his spacecraft port. How will he react when he is beyond the reassuring rhythms of the earth-moon system? How will he feel when his home planet is merely another pinpoint of light in the heavens? A distant speck indistinguishable from a star?

Perhaps the ultimate answer for man, psychologically as well as physically, is to package a portion of his accustomed world and take it into deep space with him. Imagine hurtling through a starry vacuum in surroundings that provide the comfort of a well-furnished home, with a lounge, bedrooms, and bathrooms! Huge space liners of

the 21st century might even contain aquatic gardens thriving in an artificial atmosphere duplicating earth's. The minute plants, algae and bacteria, would supply food, produce oxygen, and help clear the air of carbon dioxide.

To overcome possible detrimental effects of sustained weightlessness, the entire spacecraft might revolve, employing centrifugal force to create an artificial gravity.

If man thus carries with him a familiar environment, he may find that he has no need for the reassuring presence of the earth outside his windows — and he may find that life in space holds only minor discomforts for him as he reaches beyond the solar system.

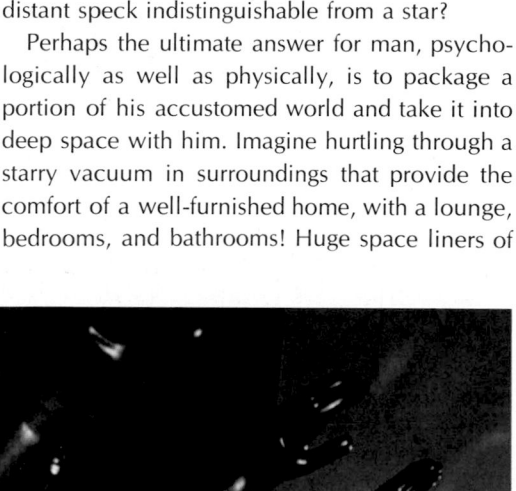

ROWS OF RUBBER GAUNTLETS *provide access to a germ-free equipment assembly chamber at McDonnell Douglas Corporation, St. Louis, Missouri. By handling space parts under sterile conditions, scientists strive to avoid the possibility that earth microbes might reach other planets — especially Mars, where life forms may exist. Below, a microbiologist examines the chamber. At Union Carbide Research Institute, Tarrytown, New York, a research assistant uses a mechanical manipulator to handle a turtle in a plastic "Mars dome" with an atmospheric pressure one-tenth that at sea level.*

SCOTT DINE (LEFT); TOM STEWART, McDONNELL DOUGLAS (BELOW); NATIONAL GEOGRAPHIC PHOTOGRAPHER ALBERT MOLDVAY

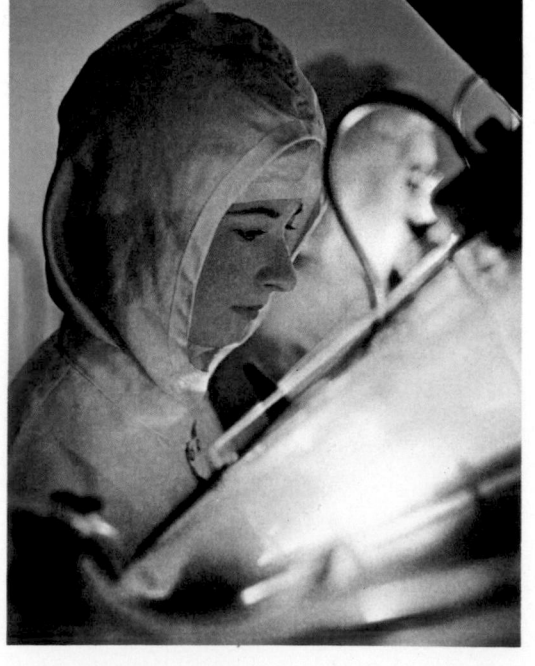

5 / VERSATILE FLYING ROBOTS WORK TO BENEFIT MAN

For the first time in history, man is able to map in detail a region he is just setting out to explore. "Columbus would be envious!" Dr. John E. Naugle, NASA's Associate Administrator for the Office of Space Science and Applications, observed in August, 1968, during a lively discussion about artificial satellites and automated spacecraft.

"Columbus and his argonauts had to start out with little more than faith. Our astronauts will travel across a well-mapped void to another world whose landscape is already familiar from pictures returned by our exploratory spacecraft."

Moving at speeds ranging from about two to five miles a second, hundreds of automated satellites, Russian and American, have orbited our planet to chart the sea of space. Sixty of these scientific explorers have probed the moon, Mars and Venus, even regions of the sun. They have radioed back information on radiation belts, the number and size of meteoroids encountered, and the extremes in space temperatures.

"Without the reassuring information these robot scouts collected for us, manned space journeys would have been considered extremely risky, perhaps delayed for a long time," Dr. Naugle said.

"Mapping that vast space ocean is only part of a comprehensive scientific and technical job that satellites have done for us," he added. "About 500 packages of instruments have faced toward earth instead of outward toward space. They have provided us with long-distance communications, advance weather information, navigation guidance, and unique views of the earth's surface.

"These automated craft have had truly dramatic impact on the world we live in. And vast new wealth may well be derived from growing industries based on satellite technology and from natural resources that remote sensors point out. When you realize how rapidly instruments and spacecraft are growing in sophistication, you know that we have just begun," Dr. Naugle said.

A sketch of the boxes of electronic instruments whirling around the earth would resemble a

LASER BEAM, *shooting past a telescope at Goddard Space Flight Center near Washington, D. C., triggers a detector aboard Explorer XXXVI some 800 miles up. In the first laser-satellite communication test in March, 1968, scientists studied effects of the atmosphere on the slender ray of light.*

diagram of electrons flying about the nucleus of a complex atom. Each package doggedly follows its set path north to south, or east to west, or somewhere in between—although the turning of the earth makes it appear that the path shifts.

Each orbiter travels at a speed dictated by its distance from earth—faster if close to earth, slower if far away. The shape of the orbit may be round, like that of the Early Bird communications satellite, or extremely elliptical like those of Russian communications satellites.

Into the newly annexed 60,000-mile extension of earth's realm, man has rocketed about 900 satellites of all kinds during the first ten years of the Space Age. Many died long ago, burned up in the lower atmosphere after losing the speed necessary to stay out of the clutches of gravity. Some, such as Vanguard I, could remain in orbit—a tiny moon of earth—for centuries.

Most of the 340 or so satellites still flying have fallen silent because of power or instrument failure, or because they were turned off by ground

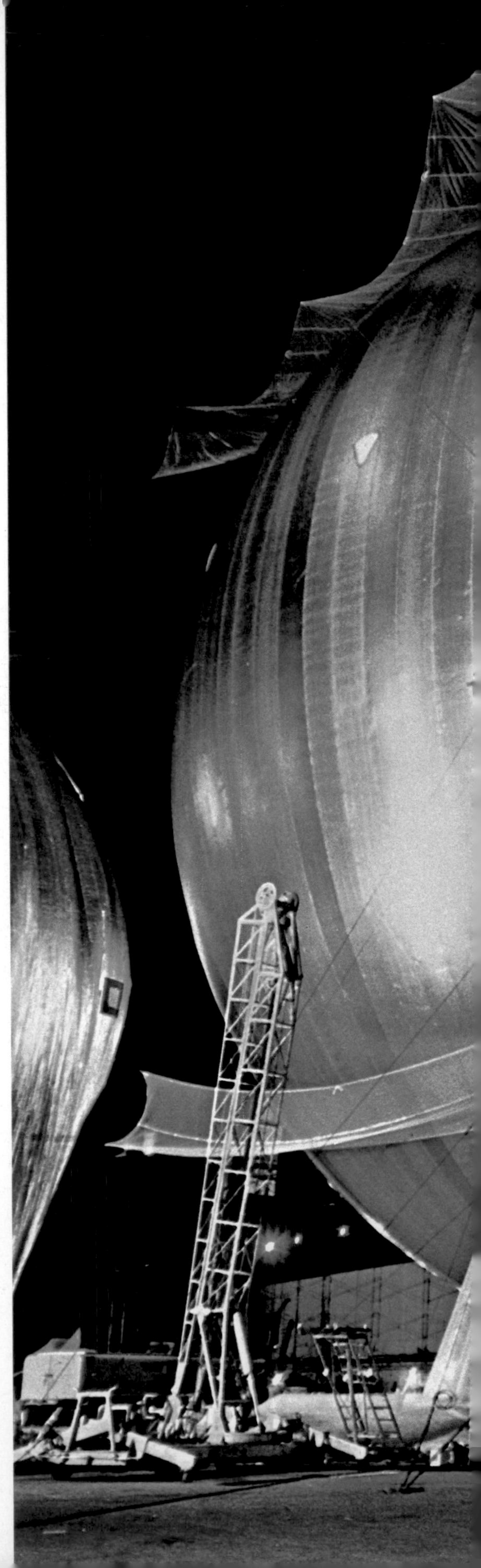

ECHO II *communications satellite balloons enormously inside a dirigible hanger at Lakehurst, New Jersey, in a prelaunch test. Boosted aloft in 1964, the plastic sphere inflated when residual air inside expanded in the vacuum of space and a powder called pyrazole, warmed by the sun's heat, turned to gas. The satellite, 135 feet across, reflected radio signals beamed from earth. Below, a backup balloon for 1960's Echo I lies in a cutaway capsule at the Smithsonian Institution, Washington, D. C.*

N.G.S. PHOTOGRAPHER JAMES E. RUSSELL (BELOW); RONALD E. CRAIG, NASA

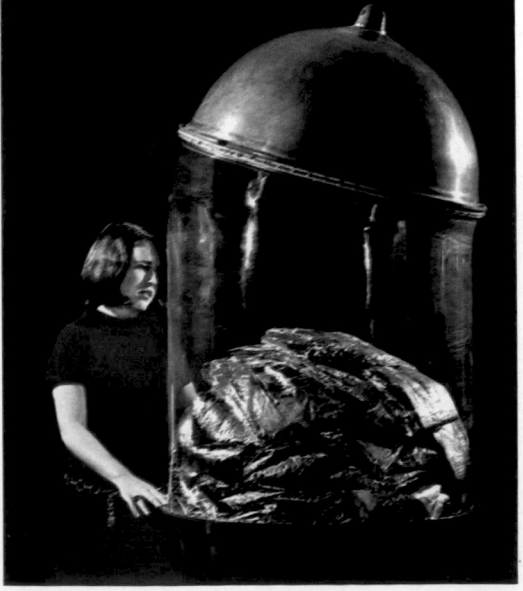

controllers in favor of newer satellites able to do a better job.

In 1968, more than 60 free-world satellites and a like number of Russian orbiters were sending their silent radio beams to receiving stations across the world—even to ships and planes. Every day satellites relay thousands of transocean conversations and feed billions of electronic bits of information onto magnetic recording tape. About 100,000 miles of such tape arrive every year at two U. S. processing stations—Goddard Space Flight Center near Washington, D. C., and the Jet Propulsion Laboratory at Pasadena, California.

From the beginning, neither the United States nor Russia wasted time rocketing empty boxes into space simply to prove that an object could be put into orbit. Sputnik I beep-beeped its way into the memory of people throughout the world as its transmitter sounded the ionosphere and made indirect measurements of space temperatures. Within minutes after launch, our tube-shaped Explorer I reported higher radiation counts above 600 miles than anyone had supposed possible.

In the first 15 months of the Space Age, the United States and Russia had sent up at least one package of instruments for nearly every kind of task that satellites perform today. By the mid-1960's, engineers in both countries had created several generations of satellites, from simple short-lived workers to highly complex and long-lived professionals with brilliant computer brains.

While the Russians concentrated until 1964 on moon probes, Venus and Mars explorations, and manned flights, the United States space program as early as 1958 began putting satellites to work for man's direct benefit.

An early task for satellites—that of communication between distant points—was first suggested in 1945 by space scientist and writer Arthur C. Clarke. Thirteen years later, Score went up hundreds of miles and broadcast President Eisenhower's Christmas message to the world.

In August, 1960, the United States launched one of the most famous objects ever to orbit the earth. Echo I, a balloon 100 feet in diameter, went into an orbit about 1,000 miles high. The silvery sphere girdled the earth every 114 minutes. Scientists beamed radio signals toward its cellophane-thin plastic sides, and thousands of miles away others tuned in the signals as they bounced off.

Between the plastic balloon of 1960 and the barrel packed with 1,200 two-way circuits scheduled for operation in 1968, a series of famous-name communications satellites have flashed across the sky and faded.

One of them was a 30-inch experimental sphere called Telstar, owned by the American Telephone and Telegraph Company and launched in July, 1962. As the first privately owned satellite reached a point in its orbit that brought the coasts of the United States and France within view, AT&T engineers began transmissions from their ground station at Andover, Maine. A fraction of a second later, a clear picture of the American flag rippling in a gentle breeze appeared on the TV screen at the Pleumeur-Bodou receiving station more than 4,200 miles away. The next day, pictures of French singing star Yves Montand came east by Telstar. Telstar worked well for four months, then stopped. Engineers kept it "repaired" a few weeks more by remote control before it ceased responding.

Recognizing the importance of world-wide communication, especially to small, remote countries, Congress in 1962 enacted a bill that led to the establishment of the Communications Satellite Corporation, or Comsat. The publicly owned corporation eventually drew more than 60 countries into a network, the International Telecommunications Satellite Consortium—Intelsat.

In April, 1965, the consortium invested in the just tested and proved synchronous satellite—the high-altitude satellite that appears to stand still. Soon after launch, Intelsat I, or Early Bird, proved itself an astonishing success.

"Overnight, its 240 voice circuits, or a color TV channel, increased transatlantic communications capacity by 50 percent," James McCormick, Comsat chairman, told me. "A set of just three high-capacity satellites, properly positioned, could put into every country's line of sight a space relay station requiring only inexpensive ground equipment with one stationary antenna."

I talked with engineers at Comsat headquarters in Washington about satellites that appear to hang in space above one spot on our planet. "With some math and physics formulas," one engineer said, "you can figure out the two magic numbers that synchronize an object with earth's speed of rotation at the Equator. To match the earth's spin rate of 1,020 miles an hour, an object orbiting the earth at the Equator must travel 6,870 miles an

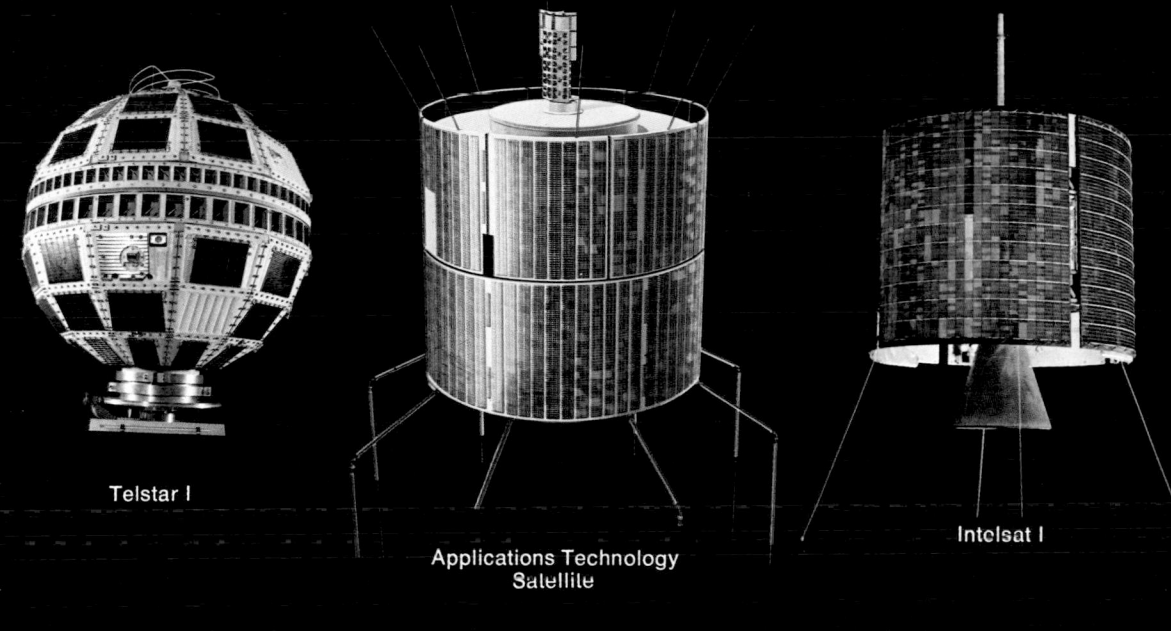

Telstar I

Applications Technology
Satellite

Intelsat I

Recovery of astronauts 600 miles south of Bermuda reaches home TV screens via Intelsat I—better known as Early Bird—orbiting 22,300 miles overhead. Gemini 7, with Frank Borman and James Lovell inside, ended its 14-day mission on December 18, 1965, after orbiting the earth 206 times. The 170-pound Telstar I, launched July 10, 1962, proved the feasibility of satellite relay communication. ATS III Applications Technology Satellite—tests equipment and techniques for orbiters of the future.

LIVE FROM CARRIER WASP

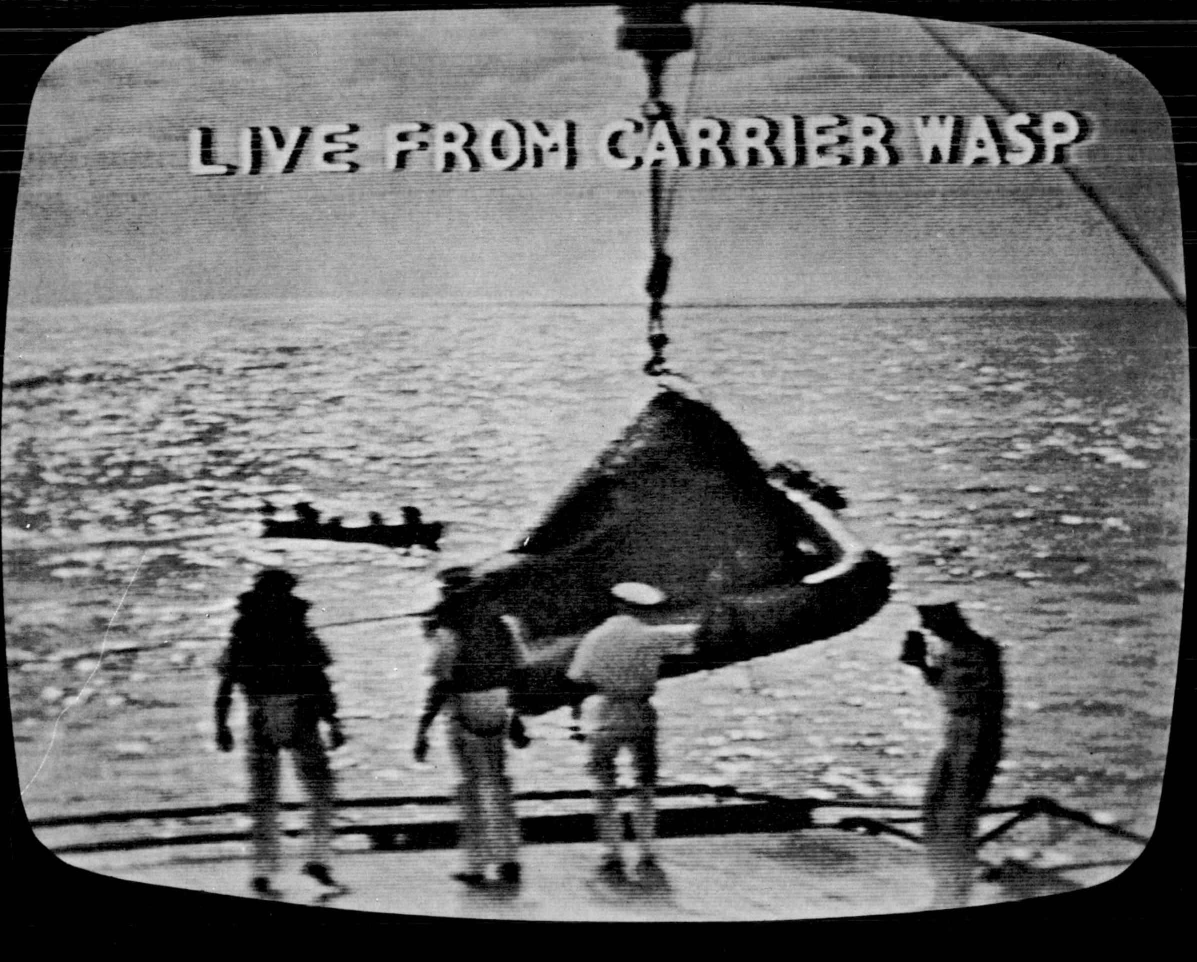

hour, one of the magic numbers, at a height of 22,300 miles, the other magic number. In 24 hours, the earth turns once and the satellite goes once around in its orbit. What the satellite does, in effect, is keep pace with a single point on the earth. Like Alice and the Red Queen in *Through the Looking Glass,* it runs hard to stand still."

Early Bird stands still over the Atlantic, working now with a partner, Intelsat II. Two more family members of the series hover over the Pacific.

"But these flying relay stations, which serve the Apollo moon program and other everyday customers, are heavily loaded with traffic," the engineer said. "We're putting up another series of bigger ones in 1968. And in 1971, in our global system we will have some 9-foot barrels with at least 6,000 two-way circuits and a seven-year life."

The U. S. military, in putting up its own set of 26 communications satellites, used several new techniques to save money: assembly-line production of identical 100-pound, top-shaped models; the launch of a number at a time with one rocket; repair by remote control.

The first set of seven went up in June, 1966, kicked one by one out of the carrier. The final eight were dropped like beads on a string along the equatorial line in June, 1968. Each satellite reports to earth how its working parts are behaving, and each has a "redundancy" section — or spare parts.

With these 26 satellites, military command posts around the world can keep in direct, private contact with each other. The next family of military satellites will permit communication between platoons in the field, aircraft, ships, mobile terminals, and large fixed terminals.

The Russians did not announce a communications satellite, their multipurpose Molniya — Lightning — until April, 1965. By the summer of 1968, eight more Molniyas had been launched. In August, the Russians announced plans for Intersputnik, a global network to rival Intelsat.

CLOUDS OBSCURE *North and South America in a portrait of earth taken on January 21, 1968, by ATS-III. Weather conditions in the United States show clearly: showers in the Southwest, clear along the lower Mississippi valley. At a height of 22,300 miles, the satellite — its orbit synchronized with the earth's rotation — remains fixed above the Equator.*

NASA, GODDARD SPACE FLIGHT CENTER

While communications satellites have brought people of widely separated countries closer together, meteorological satellites, or metsats, have saved lives and property with advance storm warnings. Cloud pictures from hundreds of miles up reveal hurricanes when they first begin to form, and follow their menacing progress day by day.

As with their comsats, the Russians did not announce a metsat, Cosmos 122, until the mid-1960's. About the same time, the United States orbited the versatile Nimbus II, designed primarily to test advanced meteorological sensors.

During the four-month life of Cosmos 122, cloud-picture exchange between the World Mete-orological Centers in Moscow and Suitland, Maryland, began over a direct cable. After sending up Cosmos 226 in June, 1968, the Russians started daily transmission of pictures—7 to 15 mosaics of large areas of the world, along with visual and verbal interpretations of the photographs.

I watched such a picture coming in from Moscow on a facsimile machine at the Suitland station just outside Washington, D. C. The paper in the machine, damp with chemicals, crept up imperceptibly as an electronic impulse burned in a line of image at a time.

"The Russians include pictures of clouds observed over their own territory," said Robert A.

ADÉLIE PENGUINS *remain unperturbed during the launch of a French Dragon rocket in 1967 from the Dumont d'Urville base near the South Magnetic Pole. The 28-foot rocket, fired 200 miles up as part of France's program of Antarctic exploration, measured electron density and recorded temperatures in the ionosphere. At right, another atmospheric probe, a helium-filled balloon at Palestine, Texas, carries equipment for studying gamma rays.*

Laudrille, Communications Manager of the National Environment Satellite Center. "Their pictures are excellent, but unfortunately their satellites do not view the entire earth daily as ours do."

A selection of cloud pictures goes every day from Suitland to Moscow, chosen from about 300 pictures daily from three ESSA satellites—Environmental Survey Satellite—operational descendants of Tiros, the Nation's experimental metsats.

These ESSA's store their pictures on magnetic tape; on command, stations at Fairbanks, Alaska, and Wallops Island, Virginia, acquire them and send them by wire to Suitland. Pieced together into one big picture, they show the cloud cover over the earth daily. Two other ESSA's transmit continuously; ground stations—and amateurs—record area pictures as the metsats pass.

Night as well as day cloud pictures came from Nimbus II during 1966. Its butterfly-like wings glittering with blue-gray solar cells, Nimbus swept around the earth about 14 times every 24 hours in a polar orbit. After the failure in late 1966 of its data-storing tape recorders, a camera continued to photograph the rotating world slice by slice. A successor with a supplementary nuclear power supply will be launched in early 1969.

Color pictures, helpful in identifying earth and cloud features, came for a time from ATS-III — Applications Technology Satellite — one of two other versatile orbiting giants. In synchronous orbit, ATS-I over the Pacific and ATS-III over the Atlantic test weather, communications, photographic, and navigational equipment. ATS cloud pictures taken every 20 minutes show the earth as a disk, and technicians project the pictures rapidly in sequence to study cloud movement.

SHEL HERSHORN, BLACK STAR; NASA

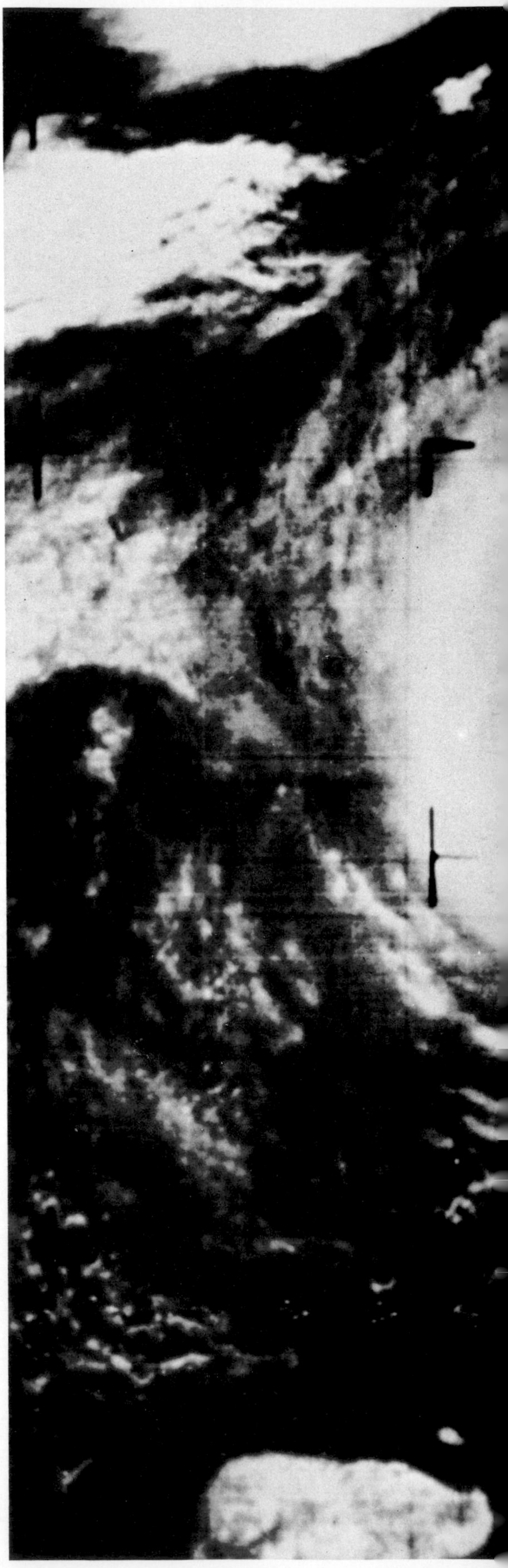

HURRICANE ALMA (right), 700 miles below the camera of Nimbus II, swirls into Florida in 1966. Above, grounded shrimpboats at Brownsville, Texas, testify to the devastating force of Hurricane Beulah in 1967. Increasingly, weather satellites help meteorologists warn of approaching storms.

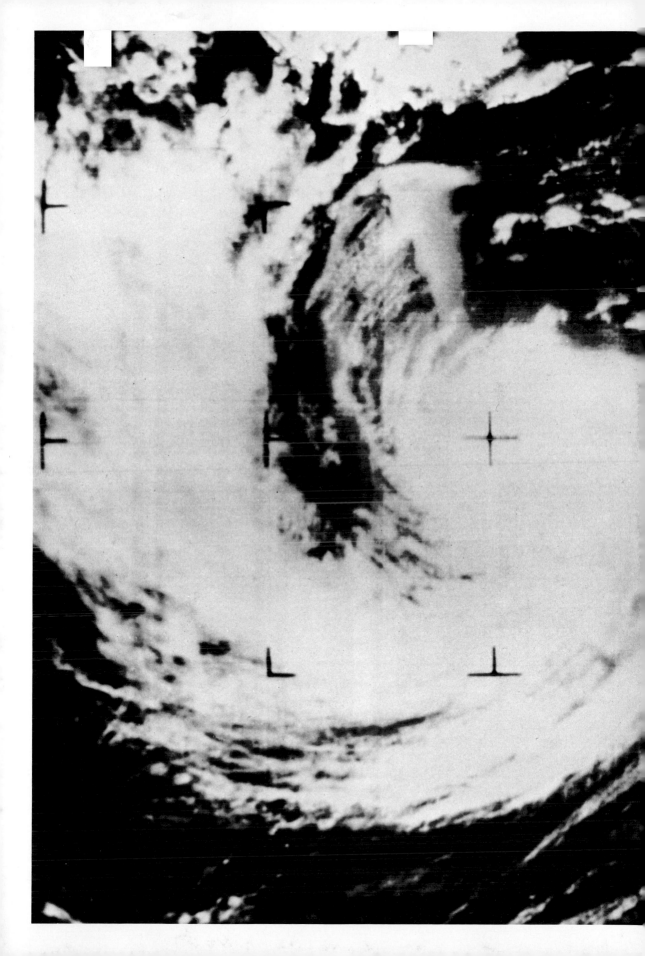

WINGLIKE SOLAR PANELS *extend from the butterfly-shaped Nimbus II weather satellite that scanned the world with four TV cameras in 1966. Three covered weather conditions over 750,000 square miles each — the fourth, a million. Eventually, three cameras stopped functioning, but one, exceeding its six-month life expectancy, continues to send pictures to NASA and meteorologists.*

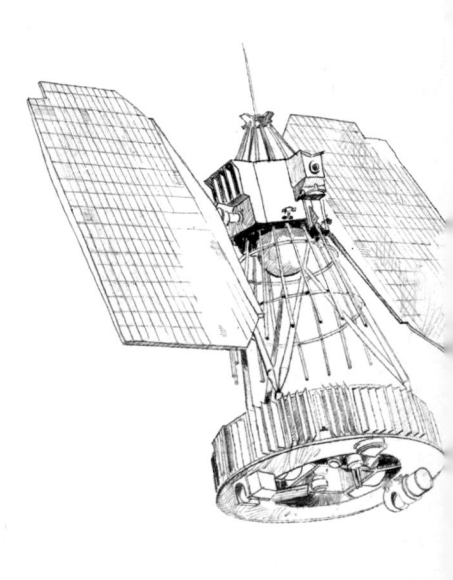

AMATEUR WEATHERMAN *John B. Tuke, manager of a civil aviation radio station in Stranraer, Scotland, stands beside his homemade weather-satellite tracking antenna. Built for about $350, the antenna receives pictures from Nimbus as it orbits overhead and records them on a phototelegraph. In addition to seeing what the earth looks like from a satellite, Tuke says, "I can confidently tell my wife to go ahead and do her washing."*

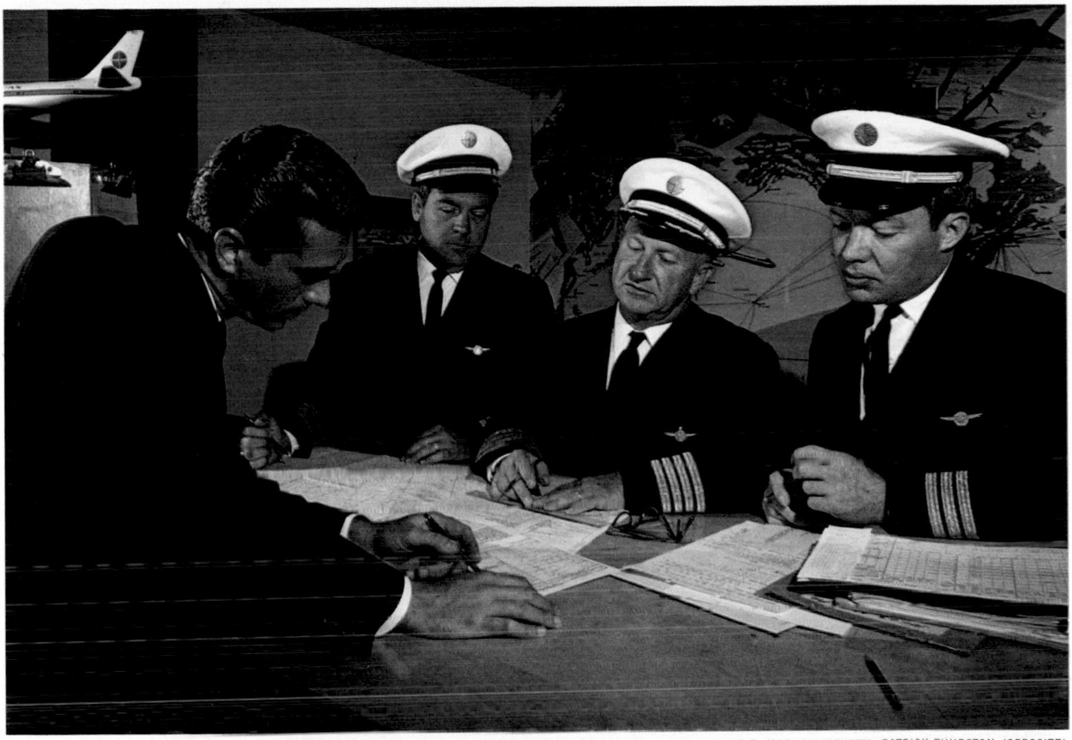

NATIONAL GEOGRAPHIC PHOTOGRAPHERS JAMES P. BLAIR (ABOVE) AND GEORGE F. MOBLEY (BELOW); PATRICK THURSTON (OPPOSITE)

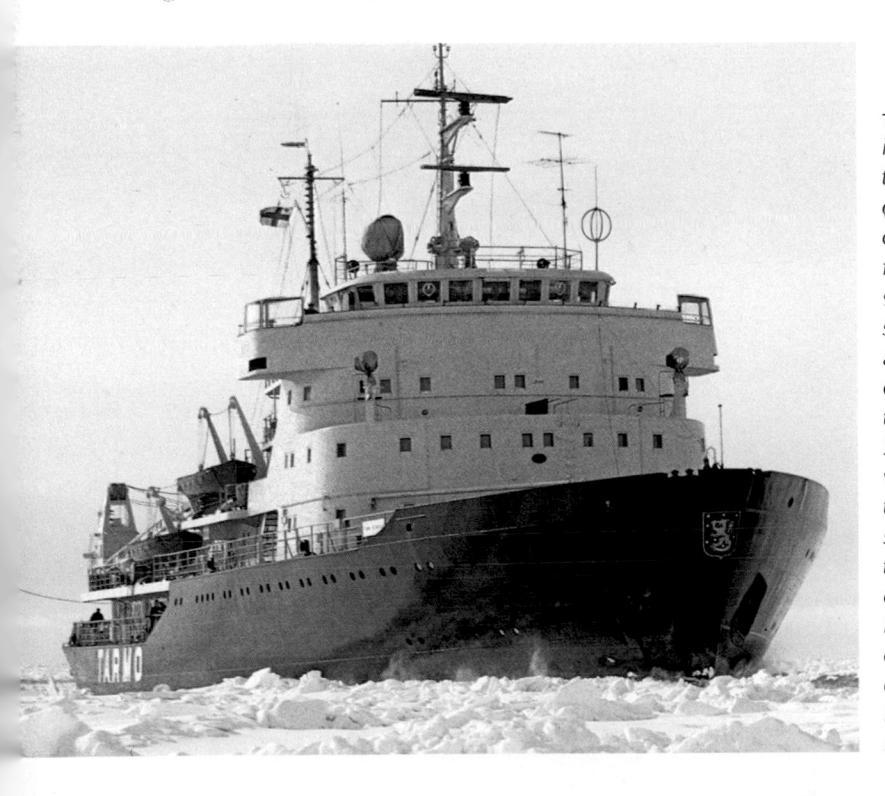

CHECKING WEATHER *conditions over the Atlantic, crew members of Pan American Airways Flight 106 receive a route plan from Joe Dodson, Operations Supervisor at Dulles International Airport outside Washington, D. C. A computer, processing data from weather satellites, radar, and ground observation, has selected the smoothest and safest course to London and Frankfurt.*

TARMO, *Finland's largest icebreaker, plows across the frozen port of Vaasa on the Gulf of Bothnia, clearing the way for the first freighters of the spring of 1967. Weather satellites, along with ships and helicopters, transmit data on ice conditions in the gulf and in the Baltic Sea to the Technical University of Helsinki and the Institute of Marine Research. During the winter, the university issues daily situation maps to icebreakers and merchant vessels. Boundaries of ice fields and breaks in the ice show clearly in the satellite pictures.*

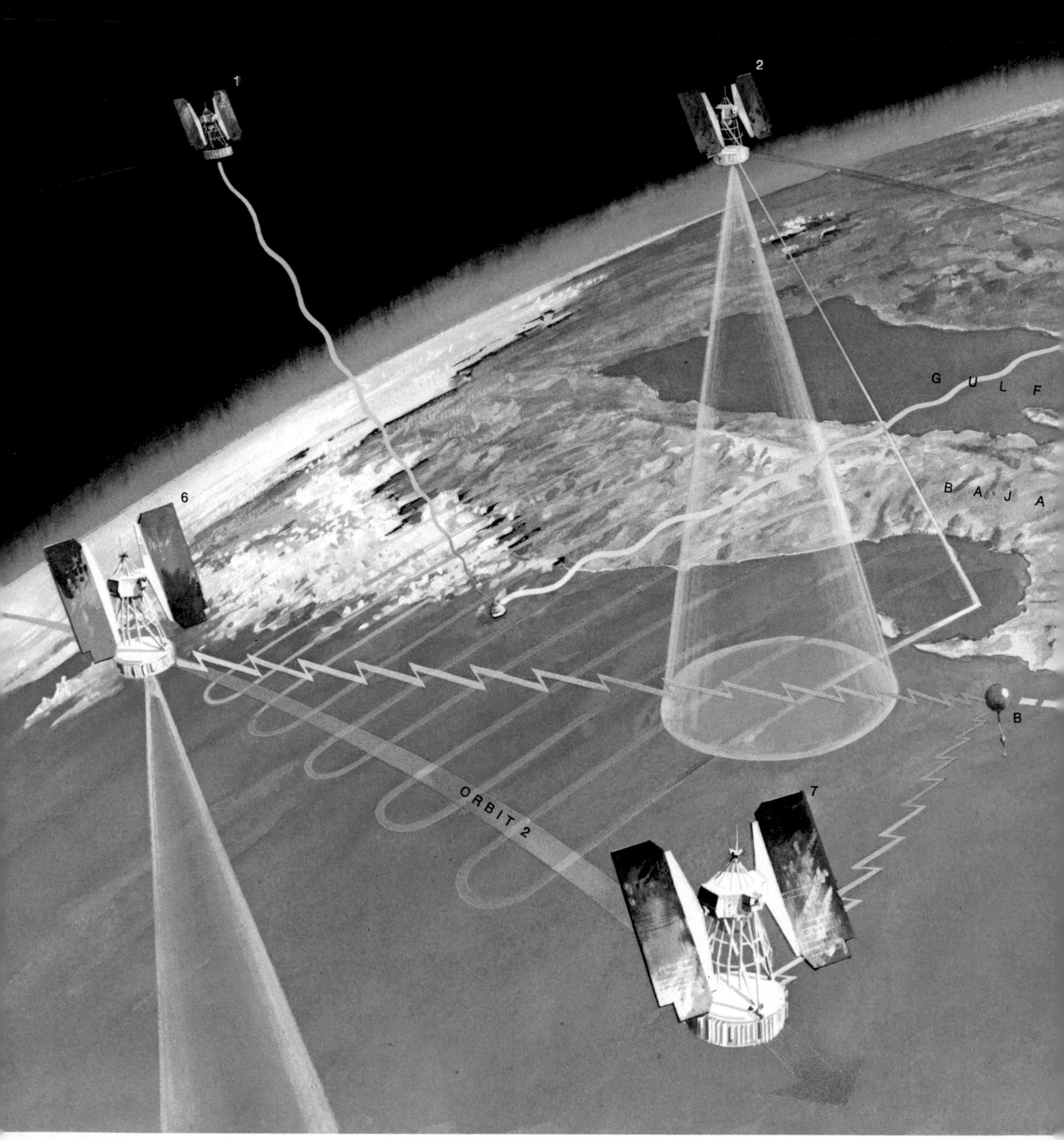

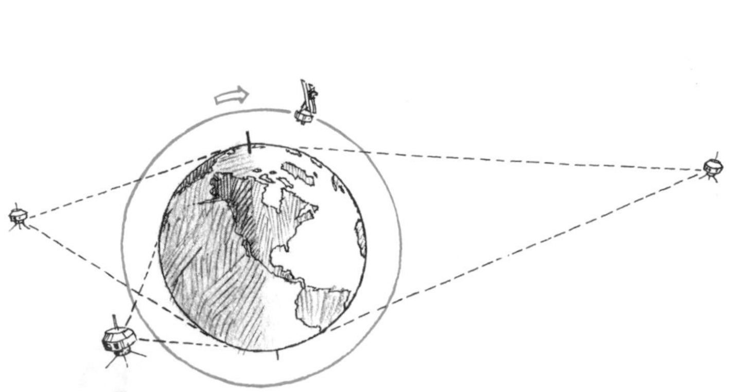

Labels in illustration: 1, 2, 6, 7, B

GULF

BAJA

ORBIT 2

WEATHER SATELLITES *in low polar and high equatorial orbits (left) will blanket the globe in the 1970's. A satellite 600 miles high will orbit 14 times from pole to pole as the earth completes one revolution; in 12 hours, all the earth's surface will move beneath it. Synchronous satellites 22,300 miles above the Equator will keep constant weather watch. Dotted lines indicate the area monitored by each orbiter.*

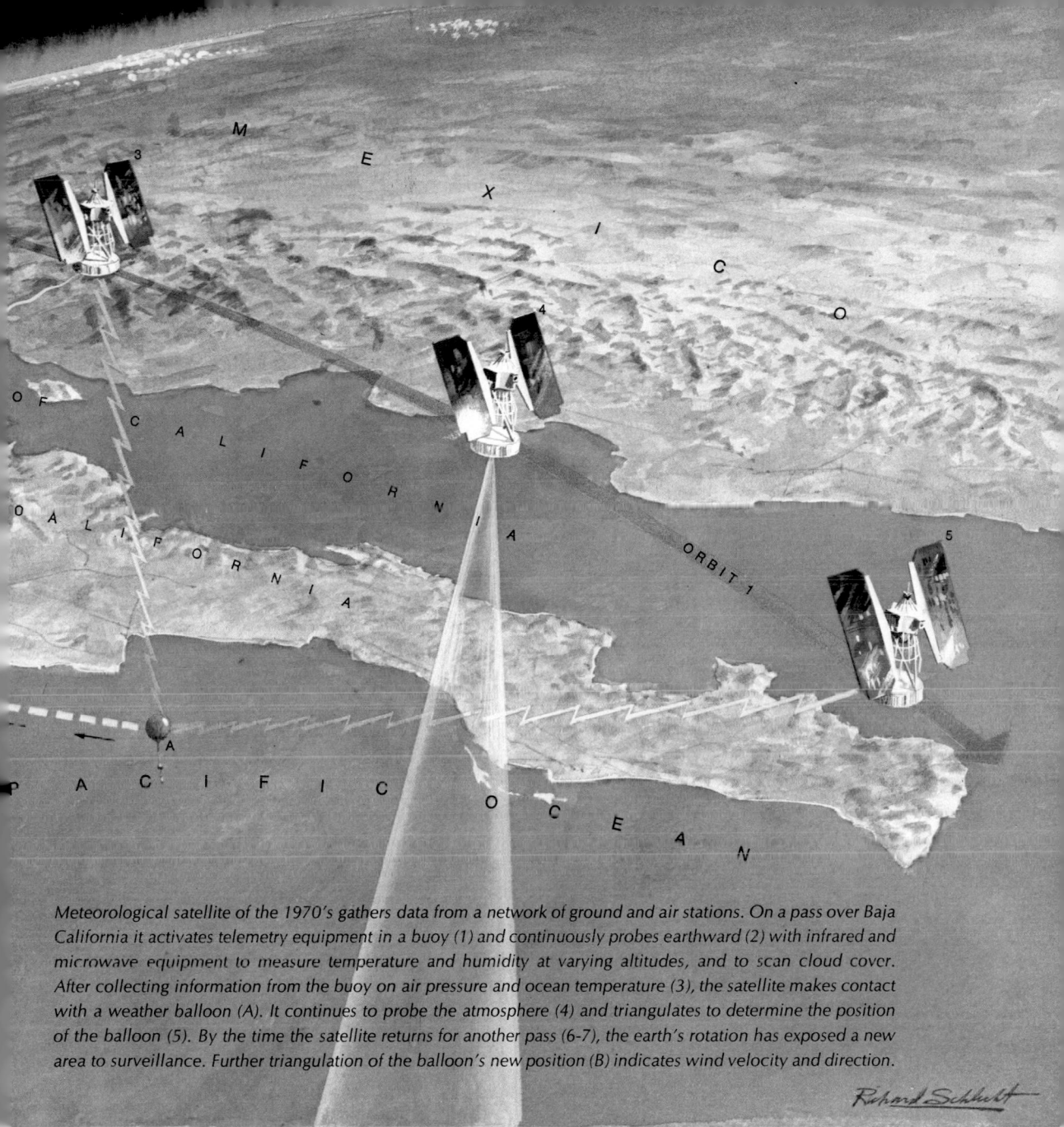

Meteorological satellite of the 1970's gathers data from a network of ground and air stations. On a pass over Baja California it activates telemetry equipment in a buoy (1) and continuously probes earthward (2) with infrared and microwave equipment to measure temperature and humidity at varying altitudes, and to scan cloud cover. After collecting information from the buoy on air pressure and ocean temperature (3), the satellite makes contact with a weather balloon (A). It continues to probe the atmosphere (4) and triangulates to determine the position of the balloon (5). By the time the satellite returns for another pass (6-7), the earth's rotation has exposed a new area to surveillance. Further triangulation of the balloon's new position (B) indicates wind velocity and direction.

Richard Schlecht

Recording images of the earth from space has become a highly developed specialty of the military. Numerous U. S. satellites use high-resolution cameras and a growing array of remote sensing instruments. The Russians have done the same with about a hundred of their 235 Cosmos satellites.

The cameras and sensors developed through military and non-military research will have many applications for civilian satellites. Scientists predict that the satellites will revolutionize activities from map-making to prospecting, from fishing to farming. The Nimbus satellite, for example, with its infrared camera for seeing clouds at night, spotted big icebergs and traced temperatures of the Gulf Stream for a thousand miles.

Sensing devices in U. S. military satellites assist in our national defense. Velas, launched in pairs to 60,000 miles, look for radiation evidence of nuclear blasts, a monitoring job that helps make effective the Nuclear Test Ban Treaty. Midas satellites detect and give early warning of missile launches. A multipurpose craft eventually will do the jobs of both these guards in the sky.

Another type of military satellite, useful for

NATIONAL GEOGRAPHIC PHOTOGRAPHER JOHN E. FLETCHER AND ARLAN R. WIKER, N.G.S. STAFF; VIRGIL H. McIE, JR., NASA, GODDARD SPACE FLIGHT CENTER

guiding submerged submarines, has been available for civilian ships and aircraft since 1967. First to use nuclear-power generators, these three Transit satellites orbit 500 miles high along a north-south polar orbit. Every two minutes, the great round boxes with extended wings beam coded radio signals to ship-borne computers that translate the information into latitude and longitude.

While satellites that resemble caldrons and cylinders and coffee grinders with wings work for people on earth, groups of purely scientific craft map space or investigate objects in our universe. Physics, astronomy, and geodetic satellites radio streams of facts thrilling to the scientist and essential to the planners of manned flight.

Explorer and Pioneer have been familiar names since the first U. S. satellite launchings. Several new families with names sounding like bits of Japanese conversation—OSO, OGO, OAO, GEOS —have joined the others in scientific exploration.

I studied a replica of Pioneer IV in the Smithsonian's collection of satellites and asked Louis R. Purnell, the spacecraft curator, how he would describe it. "Oh, it's sort of a little merry-go-round with a foot-high pointed canopy striped with gold," he said with a laugh. "Rather pretty."

Pioneer IV's rocket booster had also looked "rather pretty" when I watched it climb above old Cape Canaveral in 1959. The probe missed the moon but became the first U. S. orbiter of the sun. Now its remarkably successful grandchildren Pioneers VI, VII, and VIII report on fact-gathering missions around the sun. Since 1965, they, plus a half-dozen IMPS—a branch of the Explorer family—and five members of the new OGO group—Orbiting Geophysical Observatory—have examined cosmic rays, magnetic fields, the aurora and airglow, micrometeoroids, radio noises from space,

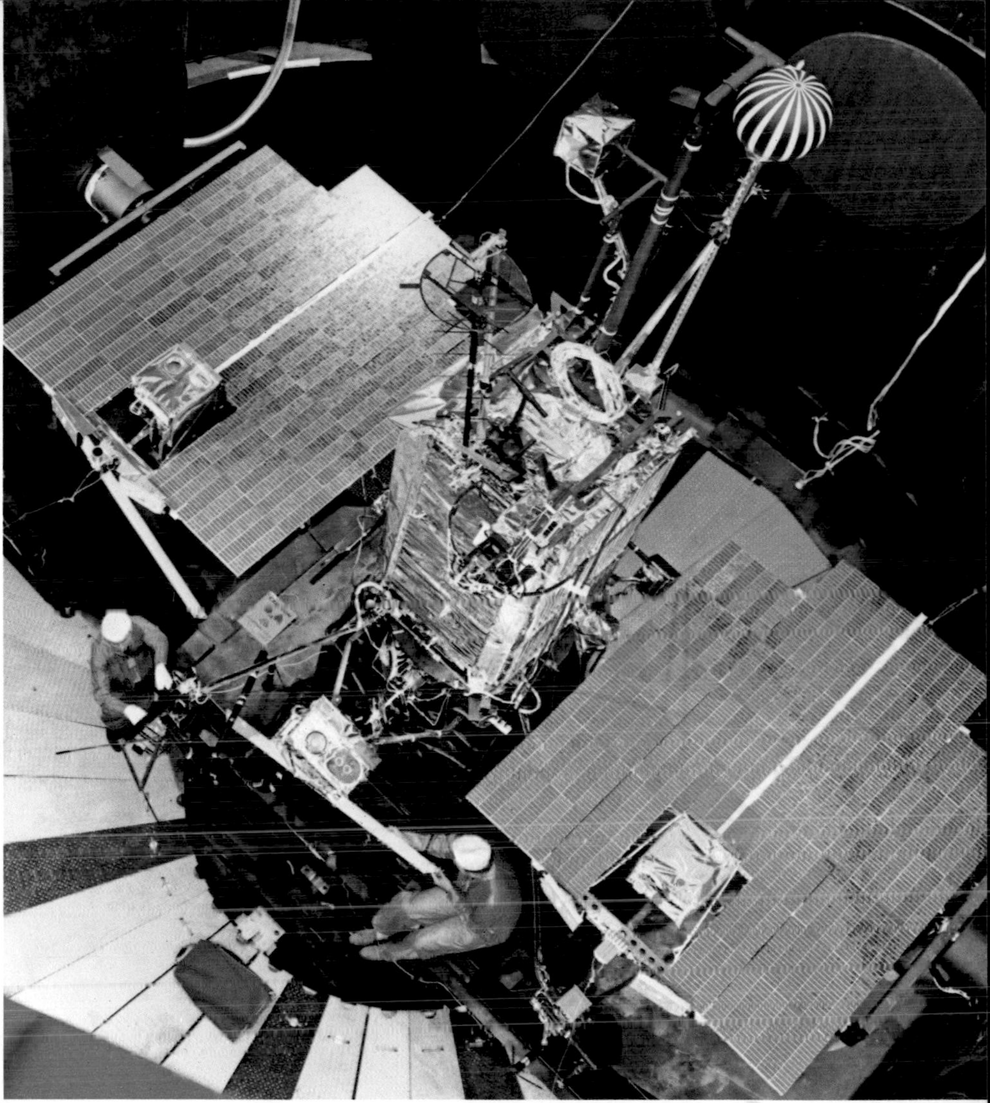

SATELLITES MUST SURVIVE *hours of demanding tests before launch. At upper left, Goddard technicians prepare an Interplanetary Monitoring Platform for the Launch Phase Simulator, a vacuum chamber on the end of a mammoth centrifuge. Inside the chamber, vibration and high-decibel sound severely jolt the craft, designed to study sun-earth relationships. An environmental simulator (right) subjects a boxlike Orbiting Geophysical Observatory and its blue solar panels to the hazards of solar radiation. OGO will study the earth's magnetosphere.*

and dozens of other phenomena. One result of the work of our robots is that charts of the Van Allen radiation belt are far more accurate than 19th-century charts of the Gulf Stream.

Members of the 40-member Explorer family do not confine their talents to physics. In geodetics, Explorer XXIX in 1965 started a mission continued by GEOS II — Geodetic Earth Orbiting Satellite —

to examine gravity and the earth's atmosphere. In astronomy, an Explorer with an X-shaped antenna 1,500 feet from tip to tip began in mid-1968 to study puzzling radio signals from space.

With scanning spectrometers, OSO — Orbiting Solar Observatory — satellites have looked straight at the sun since 1962, transmitting data that scientists transform into solar images.

"The most complex of the automated observatories," Dr. Naugle says, "is the OAO — Orbiting Astronomical Observatory. No technical challenge in the space program is more difficult." The six-sided canister with solar-cell paddles carries several telescopes. Heaviest of all U. S. satellites, it weighs more than 4,200 pounds. At launch, the first one failed; the 1968 model is expected to advance startlingly man's knowledge of the universe.

Answers to the enigmas of the stars interest the scientist primarily. But for the man in the street,

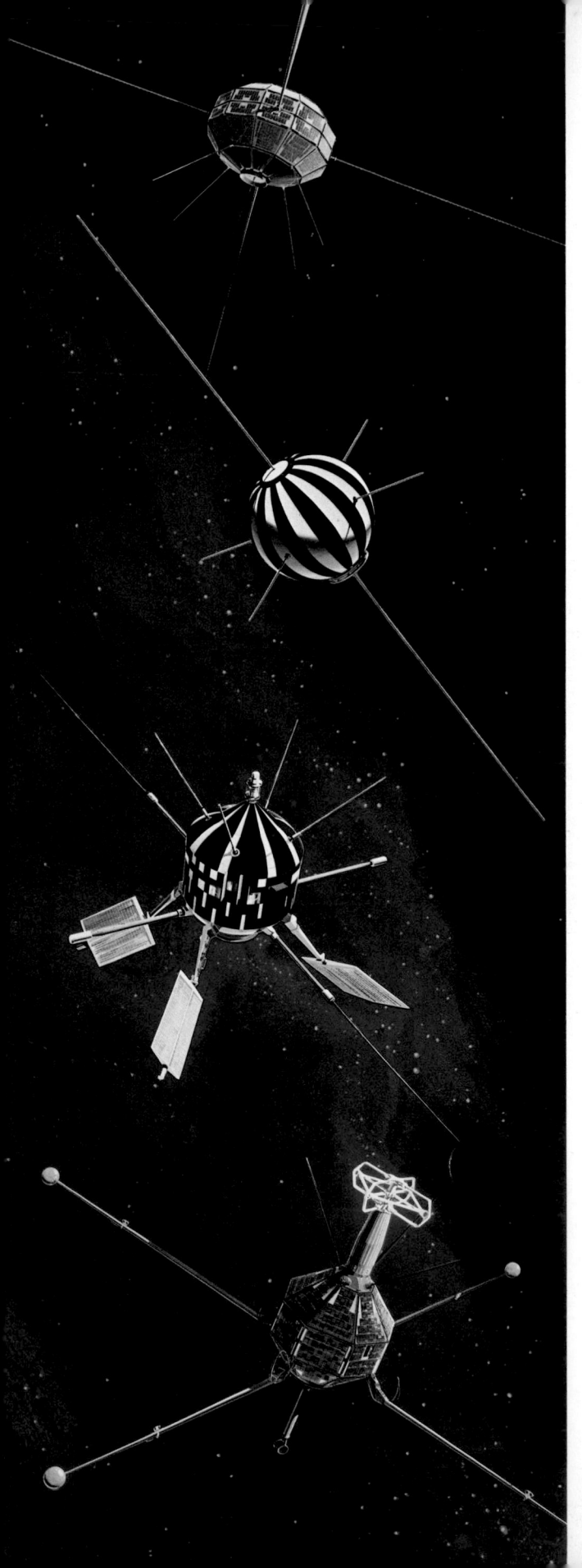

curiosity runs higher about our closest neighbor in space—the moon. What is it like? Can man go there and survive?

Both Russia and the United States lost no time in sending automated explorers to hit the moon, to fly around it, to photograph it. All our first shots failed, despite my personal encouragement. Once, for example, I persuaded a technician to stencil near the rocket's top a poetic pat from Tennyson: "After it, follow it, follow the gleam!"

The Russians, on the other hand, scored in September, 1959, when Luna II struck the moon. Three weeks later, Luna III sent back crude photographs of the far side of the moon.

The U. S. hit the moon on its eighth attempt, in April, 1962, with Ranger IV; and in July, 1964, Ranger VII succeeded in taking more than 4,300 still pictures before crashing in the Sea of Clouds.

Scientists could send a probe crashing into the moon, but could they put one there intact? Years of delay for the U. S. and failure for Russia dogged efforts at a soft-landing. Finally in February, 1966, a 220-pound Soviet automated station, round as a beachball, touched lunar soil.

During four minutes and ten seconds after impact, no one knew whether it had survived. Then, four petal-like segments of the outer shell folded down slowly, forcing a TV scanner into topmost position and allowing four antennas to extend.

SUNSPOT *the size of earth appears as a small dot against the solar surface (opposite) photographed through a 3½-inch telescope with a filter that stopped virtually all the sun's light. Because flares associated with sunspots emit short-wavelength X-rays, ultraviolet radiation, and high-energy particles that may endanger astronauts, NASA developed OSO—Orbiting Solar Observatory (opposite, lower)—to study the sun. Cape Kennedy technicians make a prelaunch check of the satellite.*

INTERNATIONAL SATELLITES *—foreign-built payloads launched by NASA—orbit the globe, adding to man's knowledge of his universe. Canadian Alouette I (top), fired aloft in 1962, investigated electron density and distribution. Candy-striped San Marco, developed by Italy, rose from a platform off the coast of Kenya in 1967. It radioed data on the equatorial atmosphere. Great Britain's Ariel II, orbited in 1964, supplemented ion, electron, and radiation studies. Ball-tipped boom antennas sprout from France's FR-IA, launched in 1965 to collect information on radio waves in the ionosphere.*

PAINTINGS BY FRANK KRASYK, NASA, GODDARD SPACE FLIGHT CENTER (LEFT); DAVID L. MOORE, NATIONAL GEOGRAPHIC STAFF (OPPOSITE, ABOVE); NATIONAL GEOGRAPHIC PHOTOGRAPHER OTIS IMBODEN

THE SUN, NUCLEAR FURNACE OF OUR SOLAR SYSTEM

Fusing at 16,000,000° C. at its core, the sun lights and sustains our world. On the solar face, the red light of hydrogen swirls about dark sunspots. A spectro-heliograph—a filter astronomers use to study separate bands of the spectrum —revealed the startling color. Each second, the sun converts 564 million tons of hydrogen into 560 million tons of helium; the remaining four million tons eventually radiate away as heat and light. For five billion years the sun has consumed itself at this rate, and scientists say it will continue for billions of years more. Solar prominences (left) often release monstrous clouds of gas that collide with the earth's magneto-sphere, sometimes disrupting radios and compasses. The largest disturbance on record, a 1946 eruption (below), spewed a billion tons of gas a million miles across the surface of the sun.

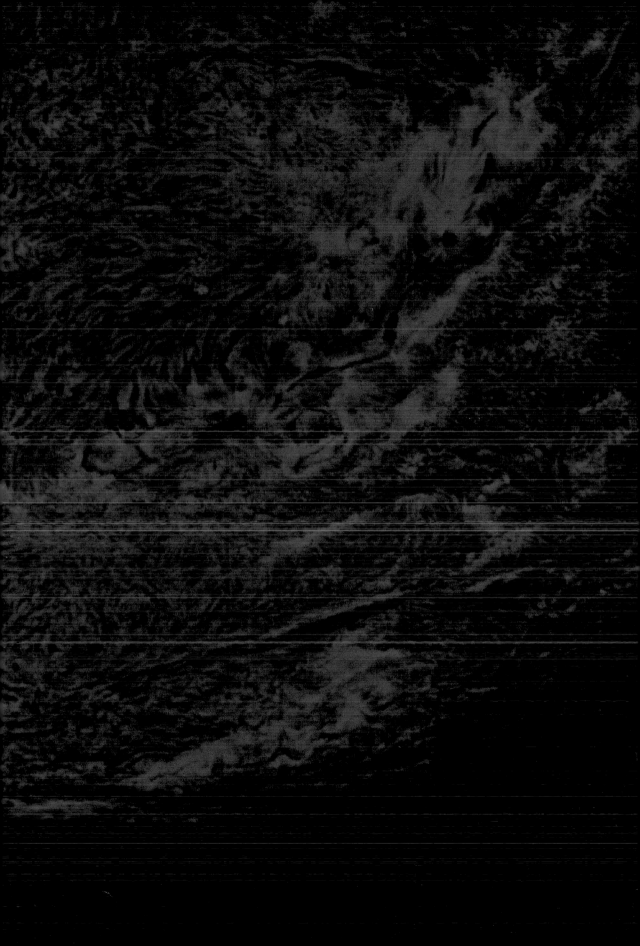

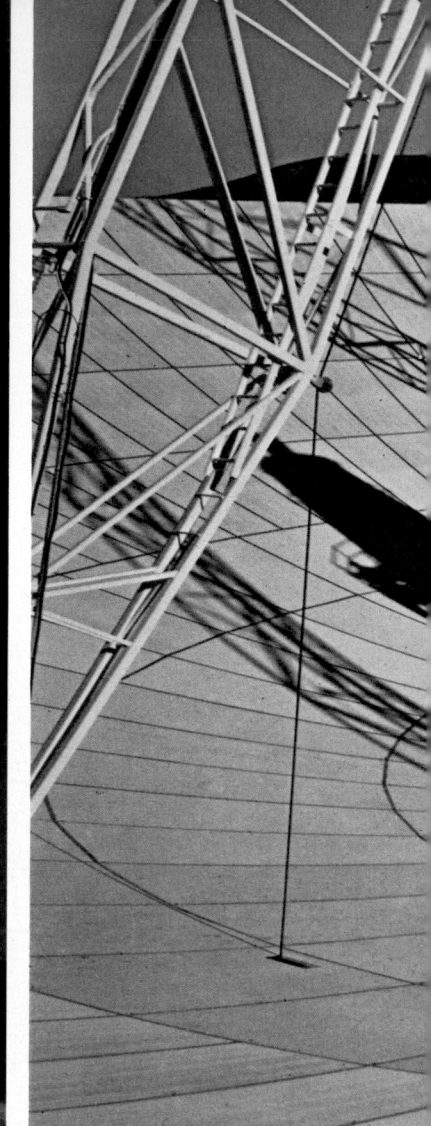

Fifteen minutes after landing, the moon station began sending signals to earth.

Five U. S. and two Russian instrument packages, including mechanical probers and diggers, dropped softly onto the moon during 1966 and 1967. Their astonishing accomplishments, and those of five Lunar Orbiters established with certainty that man could go to the moon and survive.

Dr. Naugle told Congress in 1968 after reviewing our steps toward the moon that NASA planned "three Mars fly-bys, four orbiters, and . . . two rough landers . . . by 1973."

Electronic scouts began going to Mars — and to Venus — in 1960. During the next six years, the U.S.S.R. endured a series of failures. At least 17 times the Russians launched probes. Only six got out of earth orbit and made the journey, and all six lost communication with earth before reaching

RADIO TELESCOPE *some 21 stories high rises from the Mojave Desert at the Goldstone Tracking Station, 55 miles north of Barstow, California. The 210-foot-wide, 10,000-ton "ear" can listen to radio signals three times as distant as those picked up by previous 85-foot antennas of NASA's Deep Space Network, extending satellite-tracking capabilities to the edge of the solar system. At right, engineers stand on the primary reflecting surface.*

the distant planet. One, however, did succeed in making a dead strike on Venus.

On one occasion, the Russians took what was for them an extraordinary measure to try to find out what happened to Venera I, fallen silent after traveling 4.5 million miles in space. The puzzled Russians quietly sent a delegation to England's famed radio astronomy observatory at Jodrell Bank to see if contact with Venera could be regained. It

could not. Somewhere in the terrible bake-freeze of deep space, Venera I flew on, muted forever.

During the same time that the Russians were shooting unsuccessfully for Mars and Venus, the United States triumphed with two of its four planet probes. Mariner II, after traveling for 109 days, swept within 21,600 miles of Venus in 1962.

What its instruments reported was a blow to those who had hoped the thick atmosphere might conceal some form of life. Instead, the atmosphere appeared to have a "greenhouse" effect, smothering the surface with heat at 750° F.

And the spectacularly successful Mariner IV transmitted equally startling news about Mars. On July 14, 1965, after a 228-day journey covering 3.5 million miles, the craft, resembling a big jeweled windmill, approached the great red orb. An order from earth told its TV camera to begin taking pic-

tures. Within 23 hours picture data radioed in the form of numbers convertible to shades of light and dark began to come in at the Jet Propulsion Laboratory. Over the next few days a computer translated the electronic "language" into photographs.

"When we hit frame 7, it was a very dramatic moment," said Dr. Bruce C. Murray of California Institute of Technology. "We began to recognize many, many craters. I don't think very many people had expected Mars would look like this. I think that you could quite easily be confused about whether you were looking at the moon or at Mars."

At a crowded press conference, reporters pressed for an answer to a centuries-old question: Was there any evidence of life on Mars? No, the scientists replied, but we can't expect that kind of detail from a few Mariner pictures. Even earth, photographed thousands of times by metsats,

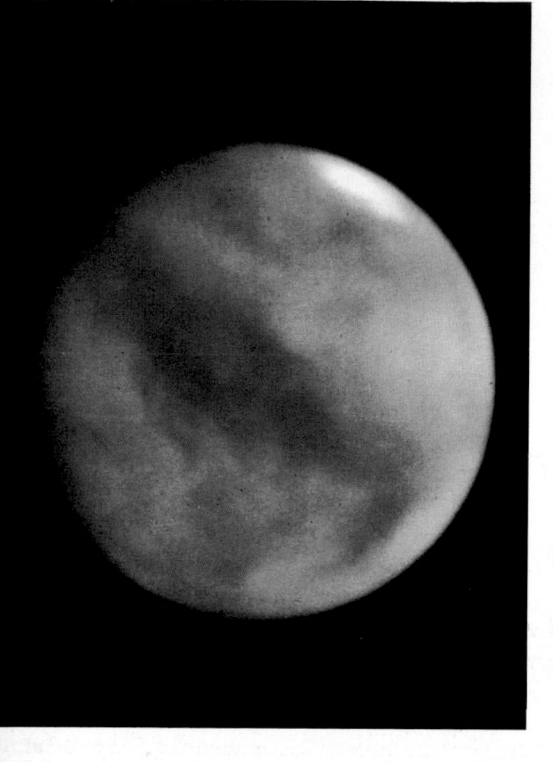

WELL-DEFINED CRATERS, *three to four miles across, scar the Martian surface in the 11th of 21 photographs taken by Mariner IV on July 14, 1965. The craters—much like the moon's—surprised many scientists who expected a more earthlike landscape. In the most detailed picture previously possible (left), the red planet glows through earth's distorting atmosphere in a photograph taken with* the 60-inch Mount Wilson telescope. At right, technicians at Pasadena's Jet Propulsion Laboratory prepare Mariner for temperature tests inside a space simulator. Aboard the spacecraft, 28,224 solar cells converted sunlight into 700 watts of electricity to power all of Mariner's equipment. Radio signals carrying picture data required 12 minutes to cross the 134 million miles to earth.

rarely reveals evidence of intelligent life. And for Mars there exist only 21 pictures.

The Russians finally had their V-for-Venus day on October 18, 1967. Venera IV, still in radio contact with earth, arrived near our brightest planet after a four-month trip. It ejected a 40-inch egg-shaped package that began to descend through the alien atmosphere. The Venera space bus burned in the intense heat of entry, but the heavily insulated capsule drifted down by parachute.

As this contraption was tossed by winds of greater than hurricane force and broiled by the intense heat, it took a wide range of readings. For 96 minutes, it radioed to earth a story of a strangely hostile Venusian atmosphere. Cloud temperatures: 104° to 536° F. Atmosphere: 98.5 percent carbon dioxide, no nitrogen. Surface pressure: 15 times that of earth. Suddenly the signals stopped. Just why they stopped, and at what point in the cap-

sule's descent, is still argued among scientists.

So, our robots appear to tell us, Mars may be the more hospitable planet. But before the red planet becomes host to man, no doubt an ingeniously designed robot will land there. And the history books may give the name—not of a Columbus, but of some inanimate and ungainly package as the first visitor from earth.

For the artful robots, tougher than the tender chemistry of man, are daily becoming more manlike in their performance in space. They watch our weather. They photograph our land. They guide our ships at sea. We can sometimes follow their eerie tracks as they carry words and pictures across the night sky from one side of the earth to the other. Silent and solitary as celestial specters, they go tirelessly about their duties. Perhaps someday they will tell us that the flower of earth is not the only flower of life in the vast fields of space.

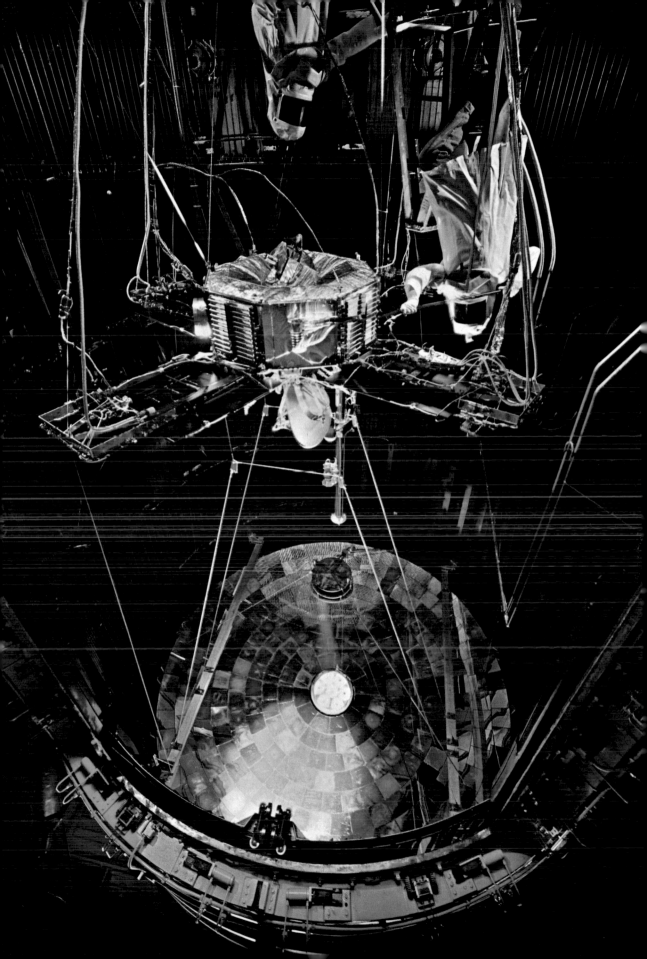

6/ CAMERAS OF THE COSMOS; THE VIEW FROM SPACE

The human eye—unlike a camera—leaves no permanent record, but it is, so far, the most nearly perfect instrument for giving the world its own image from the lofty reaches of space.

When Gordon Cooper returned from his first orbital flight in 1963, he described a totally unexpected view of the earth. In his official flight report the quiet, slow-talking Oklahoman said:

"I could detect individual houses and streets in the low-humidity and cloudless areas such as the Himalaya . . . area, the Tibetan plain, and the southwestern desert area of the U. S. I saw several individual houses with smoke coming from the chimneys in the high country around the Himalayas. . . . I saw what I took to be a vehicle along a road in the Himalaya area and in the west Texas-Arizona area. I could first see the dust blowing off the road, then could see the road clearly, and when the light was right, an object that was probably a vehicle. I saw a steam locomotive by seeing the smoke first. . . . I also saw the wake of a boat in a large river in the Burma-India area."

In addition to having remarkably good eyesight, Cooper possesses one quality in extraordinary measure—the rare gift of a penetrating and perceptive curiosity combined with the capacity to pay extremely close attention to whatever grips his interest. I recall asking him one evening what he found most interesting on the dark side of the earth during his 22 orbital nights.

"Well, I could see the lightning in thunderstorms very clearly," he told me, "but the most fascinating things were meteoroids striking the earth's atmosphere. I could just sit there and look down on them coming in from all directions—big ones and little ones, in short streaks and long streaks. Once, I saw a big one that came in to the side of the earth and seemed to be heading straight up toward me. Then it appeared to burn out."

Cosmonaut Gherman Titov—a lifelong admirer of the Russian poet Alexander Pushkin—gave us a vivid verbal picture of his ascent into space:

"Like a motion picture camera that speeded up

INDIAN SUBCONTINENT *sprawls 622 miles below Gemini 11, September 14, 1966. An 8-foot antenna protrudes in the foreground. Thousands of such photographs, taken during manned and unmanned missions, give oceanographers, weathermen, and geographers valuable new views of our planet.*

RICHARD F. GORDON, JR., GEMINI 11, NASA

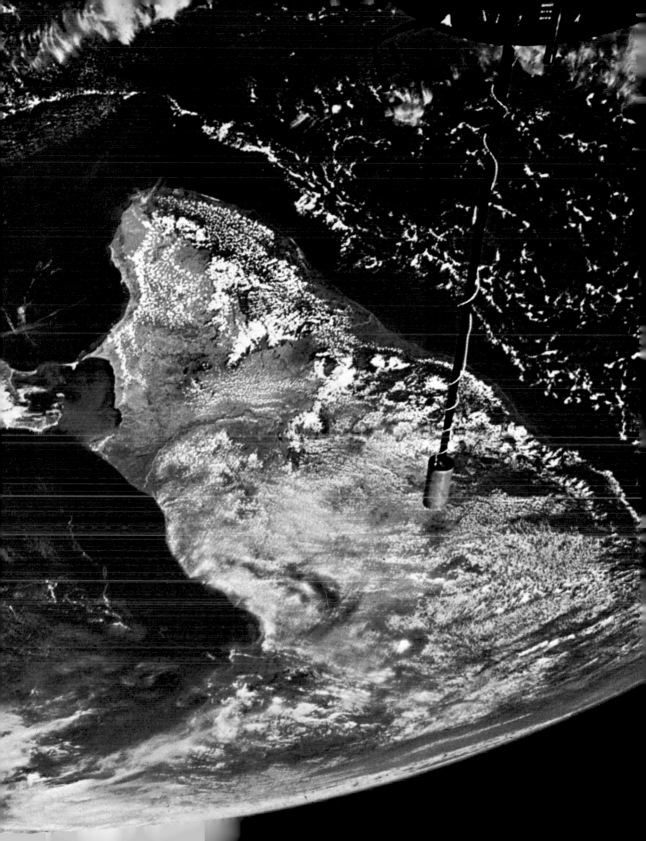

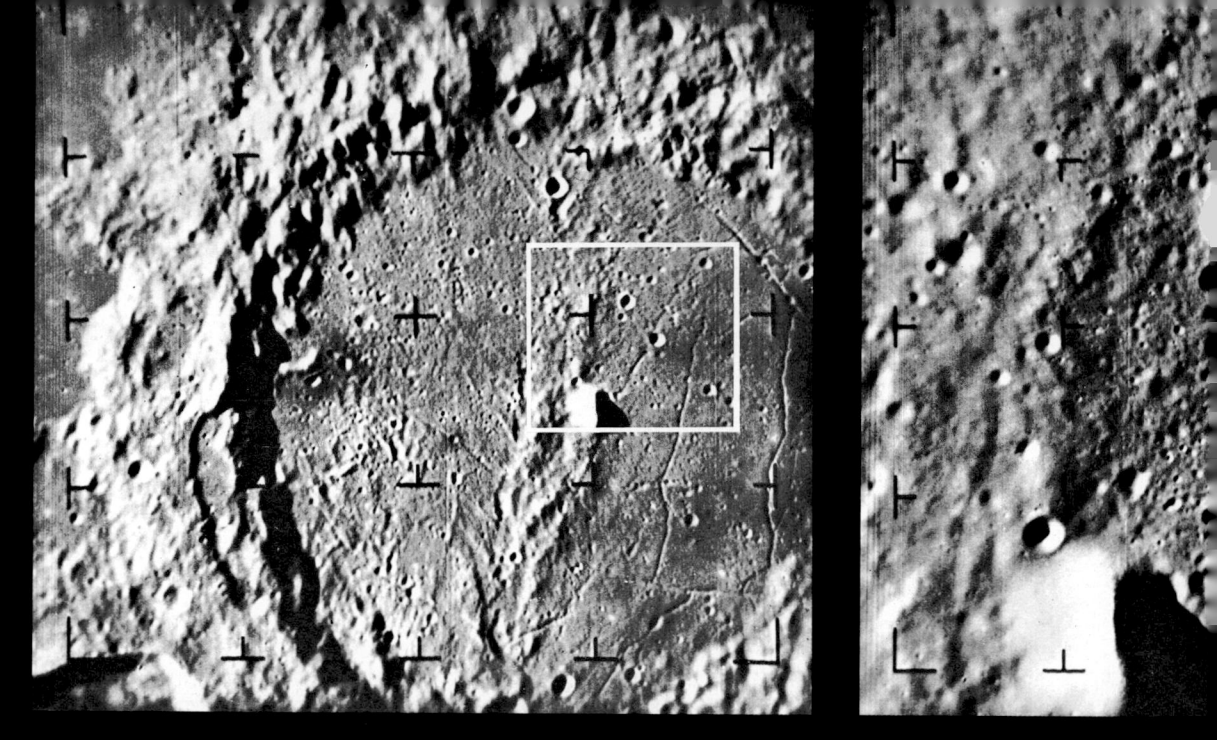

Huge crater Alphonsus looms before the cameras of Ranger IX, hurtling toward the moon at 6,000 miles an hour. Launched from Cape Kennedy the afternoon of March 21, 1965, the craft began transmitting pictures some 65 hours later; within 20 minutes—before impact just three miles from its intended target—Ranger IX sent 5,814 pictures "live from the moon" to television screens on earth. The central peak of the 70-mile-wide crater rises 3,300 feet.

enormously, the darkened side of mountains sprang magically to life as my continuing ascent and increasing velocity scattered sunlight in all directions. I stared at plowed fields that shone with a deep blue-black color . . . at lemon-colored fields of harvested wheat, and at forests of deep smoke-green that seemed to float past the porthole. The clouds drifting above them were amazingly sharp and clear in their definition, like wind-filled sails hanging just above the surface. . . . The earth flashed as a million-faceted gem, an extraordinary array of vivid hues that were strangely gentle in their play across the receding surface of the world."

That imitation of the human eye, the camera, cannot express enthusiasm, but the accurate, permanent, and sometimes magnified impression it gives us from space not only generates enthusiasm in the viewer, it also provides us with startling new facts about the earth, the moon, and the planets. In fact, wherever man sends space ships, he also sends still, motion picture, and television cameras. Just as the world saw the first astronauts

and cosmonauts as they actually appeared in orbit, so shall we witness, through the electronic legerdemain of the television camera, the moment man places the first tentative footstep upon the surface of the moon.

An initial and compelling photographic objective in space was to discover what the moon looks like in close-up. We needed to document general information useful to lunar scholars, and, more imperatively, to determine the nature of the lunar surface to guide scientists and engineers in the design of the moon-bound Apollo spacecraft. Without such knowledge, the specifications of the lunar module might be incorrect. The development of the four saucer-shaped footpads, for example, might be based on a faulty estimate of the bearing strength of the moon's surface.

To find the answers, the United States devised, first of all, the Ranger program for hard-landing on the moon. The Jet Propulsion Laboratory at Pasadena, California, spent the better part of five years and more than $200,000,000 on the series of ambitious flights necessary to acquire preliminary

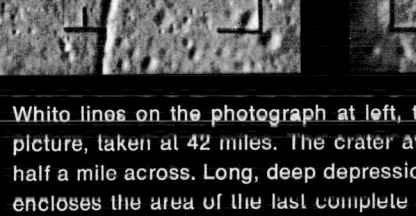

White lines on the photograph at left, taken from 163 miles, mark the area of the center picture, taken at 42 miles. The crater at the upper right of the square measures less than half a mile across. Long, deep depressions called rills furrow the surface. The small square encloses the area of the last complete image (right), transmitted from 4.47 miles seconds before impact at the spot marked by the arrow. Craters 40 feet wide appear pinhole size.

closeup views of our nearest neighbor in space.

Prior to Ranger, according to astrogeologist Eugene M. Shoemaker, ". . . we had gone about as far as we could in discerning lunar topographic features with earth-based optics. Our best telescopes had brought us visually to within 400 miles of the moon's surface. But they could do no more. The protective atmosphere that shields us from the blaze and bombardment of the universe also shields its secrets from us; our vision is blurred. No lunar detail less than 800 feet across had been distinguished from our planet."

The plan for Ranger VII was a bold one. An Atlas-Agena-B rocket combination would put the 800-pound probe on a collision course for the plainlike region 390 miles south of the great crater Copernicus. Just minutes before the spacecraft's impact, six television cameras would record their historic view, then quickly transmit their impressions to earth before being dashed to pieces on the moon.

As dawn broke over the West Coast on July 31, 1964, sleepless personnel in space centers from coast to coast waited expectantly. At the Jet Propulsion Laboratory secretaries came to work two hours early to witness the climax of the 67-hour flight. Known to all was the fact that, after six Ranger missions had fallen short of the ultimate objective, Ranger VII was now approaching the moon with cameras ready. Seventeen minutes before impact, shutters opened to allow new-moon images to form in Ranger's TV tubes. These images, in the form of electrical impulses, were flashed instantly to the Goldstone tracking station in California's Mojave Desert.

A hot line from Goldstone to JPL passed the first word that the pictures were coming in. Finally, the voice on the hot line said ". . . 10 seconds . . . we're receiving pictures to the end . . . impact . . . impact!"

The sudden silence was followed by shouts, handshakes, tears of relief, and wild cheering. America's photographic mission to the moon was a success.

The 4,300 images transmitted in those final

(Continued on page 132)

"Picture of the century." Space scientists thus hail this oblique view of the moon crater Copernicus, photographed by Lunar Orbiter II as the satellite swept past just 28.4 miles high on November 23, 1966. Mountains rise as high as 2,700 feet from the crater's floor.

NATIONAL AERONAUTICS AND SPACE ADMINISTRATION

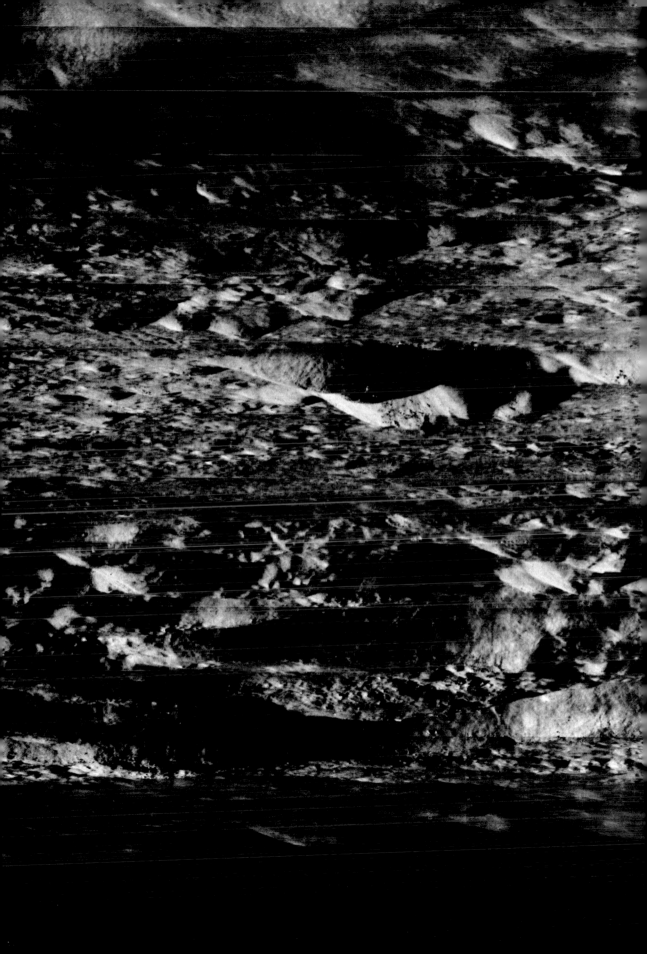

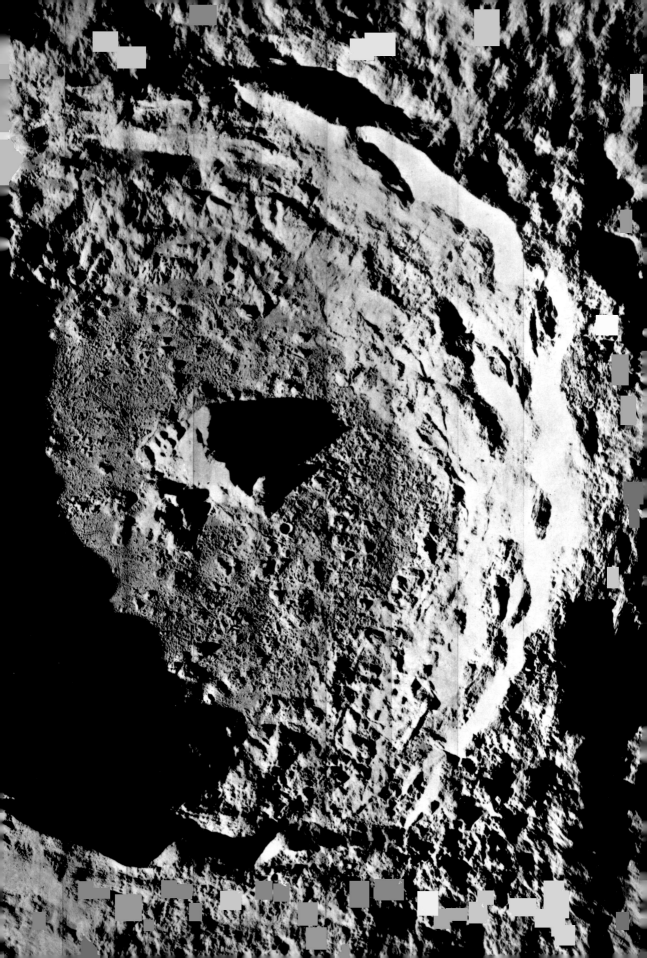

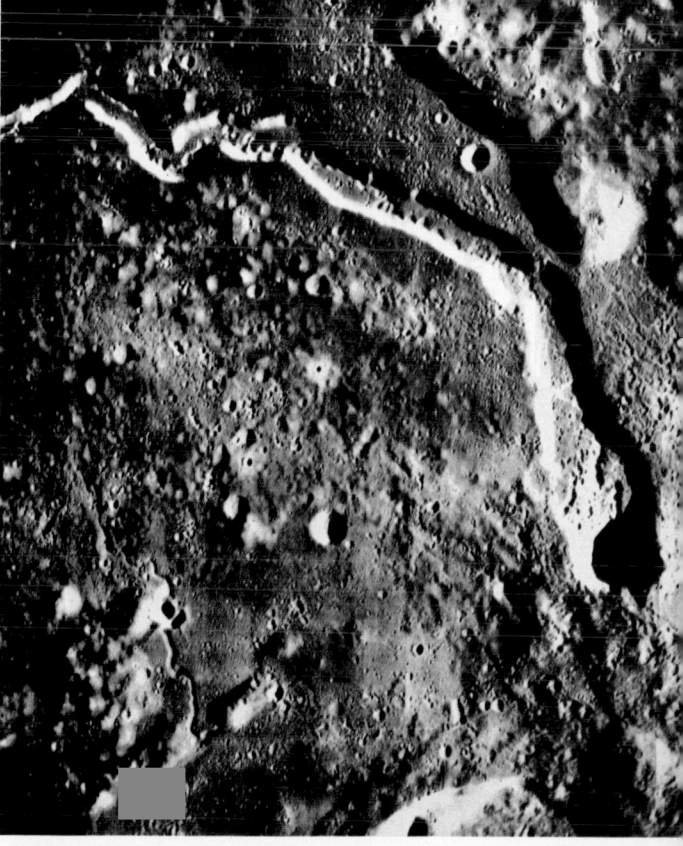

A GREAT LUNAR CRATER
AND A MYSTERIOUS VALLEY

Bowl-shaped Tycho crater, 54 miles from rim to rim, holds high terraced walls and a mountain that soars more than 7,000 feet. Lunar Orbiter V, sweeping above the moon's southern uplands in August, 1967, photographed the terrain through a wide-angle lens from a height of 135 miles. Hundreds of mounds — possibly volcanic domes — dot the crater's floor. Some 1,400 miles northwest of Tycho, snakelike Schröter's Valley (below) starts in a wide area called Cobra-Head and trails diagonally across the picture. A deep, narrow inner rill — first revealed by Lunar Orbiter V — slopes down from the Cobra-Head and meanders the length of the main valley. About a hundred such lunar rills lead a growing school of scientists to theorize that eons ago some fluid — perhaps water — may have carried fine-grain debris that eroded the channels. Some experts believe water may still exist on the moon below the surface or in the form of ice at the poles.

NASA, PRINTS FROM ARMY MAP SERVICE

ASTRONAUTS IN A SPACE AGE BUG

WILL TOUCH DOWN ON THE MOON

WITHIN AN OVAL LANDING SITE

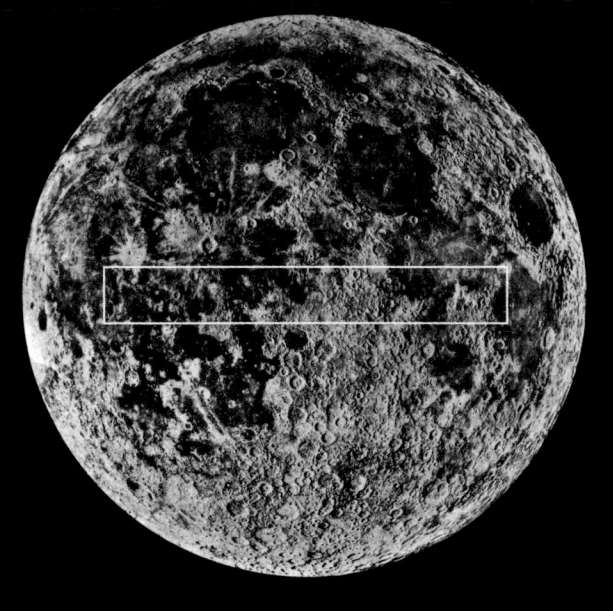

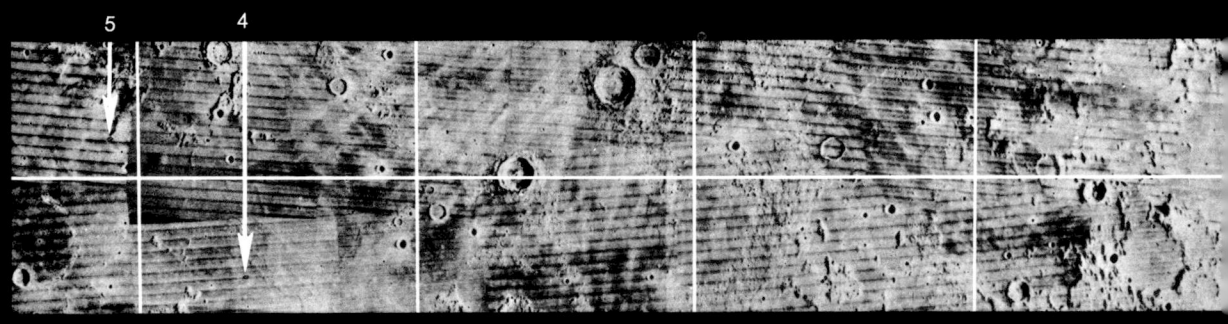

Spindly-legged craft carrying U.S. Apollo astronauts will settle onto the moon within one of five oval areas near the lunar equator. Red dots (with arrows) locate the sites within a mosaic strip map that corresponds to the outlined region at left. Lunar Orbiter satellites photographed the area—the Apollo Zone of Interest—in 1966 and 1967 while traveling in elliptical orbits that brought cameras within 25 miles of the surface. After studying thousands of photographs, scientists and engineers of the National Aeronautics and Space Administration selected the three-by-five-mile sites, each relatively flat and rubble-free. Time of lift-off through the launch window—a monthly interval when earth and moon are in proper alignment—will determine the landing area used. If Apollo streaks upward from Cape Kennedy early in the six-day period, the astronauts will land in the Sea of Tranquillity (1 or 2). A delay of two or three days will put them in the Central Bay (3), and a delay of four to six days will dictate a landing in the Ocean of Storms (4 or 5). Lunar Orbiter spacecraft photographed nearly all the moon's surface—including the far side—making possible new maps with as much as 100 times the detail available from earth-based observation.

U. S. AIR FORCE, AERONAUTICAL CHART AND INFORMATION CENTER
(ABOVE LEFT) AND NASA, PRINTS FROM ARMY MAP SERVICE

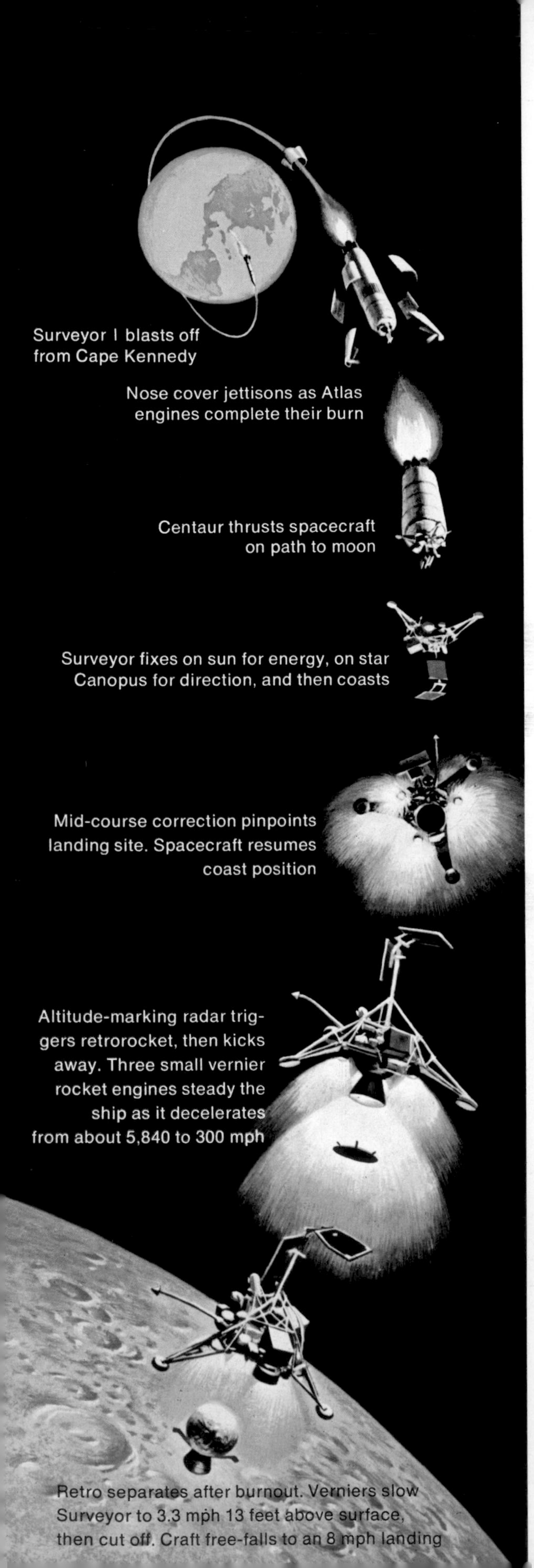

Surveyor I blasts off
from Cape Kennedy

Nose cover jettisons as Atlas
engines complete their burn

Centaur thrusts spacecraft
on path to moon

Surveyor fixes on sun for energy, on star
Canopus for direction, and then coasts

Mid-course correction pinpoints
landing site. Spacecraft resumes
coast position

Altitude-marking radar triggers retrorocket, then kicks
away. Three small vernier
rocket engines steady the
ship as it decelerates
from about 5,840 to 300 mph

Retro separates after burnout. Verniers slow
Surveyor to 3.3 mph 13 feet above surface,
then cut off. Craft free-falls to an 8 mph landing

PLACING CANDID CAMERAS
ON THE MOON'S DESOLATE FACE

*Bridging a quarter-million-mile gulf from earth,
Surveyor I journeys to the moon to investigate the
lunar terrain. Between May 30, 1966, and January 7, 1968, NASA launched seven Surveyors and
received 89,000 pictures. Below, an engineer of
the Hughes Aircraft Company, builder of the vehicles for NASA's Jet Propulsion Laboratory, inspects
the nozzle of a vernier engine that helps control
the craft in flight and slow it during descent; the
globular tank holds helium to pressure fuel into
the engines. In California's San Gabriel Mountains,
specialists check one of the spacecraft. The blue
panel mounted on the mast contains 3,960 solar
cells that convert the sun's energy into electrical
power. The square antenna behind the solar panel
receives command signals from ground controllers
and transmits picture data to earth. Mounted on a
turret below the right side of the panel, the robot's
television camera searches the ground and scans
the horizon. Surveyor landings showed that astronauts can safely set foot on a firm lunar surface.*

DIAGRAM BY DAVIS MELTZER © N.G.S. (LEFT); HUGHES AIRCRAFT COMPANY

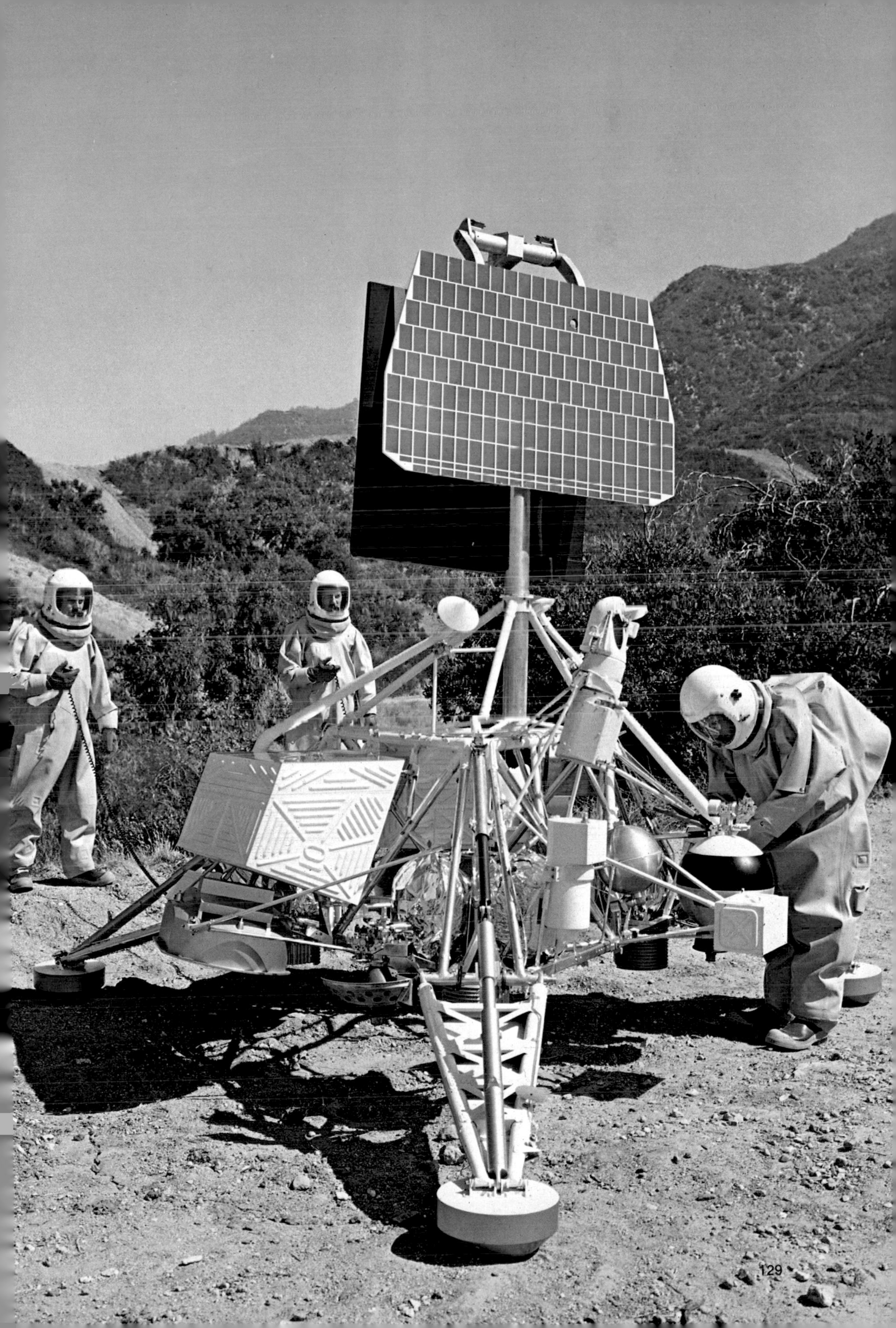

HUGHES AIRCRAFT COMPANY

SCIENTISTS CAREFULLY EXAMINE
A SURVEYOR BEFORE LAUNCH

*Three-legged robot squats beneath the giant solar
vacuum test facility (above) at Hughes Aircraft
Company's space environmental laboratory in El
Segundo, California. Like a team of surgeons, white-
gowned engineers surround Surveyor (right) before
the hydraulic lift eases it into the chamber. Lamps
in the facility simulate the radiation of sunlight in
space. Temperatures varying from −250° to 250° F.
match the lunar night and day. The first Surveyor
to reach the moon survived temperature extremes
there for seven months before falling silent.*

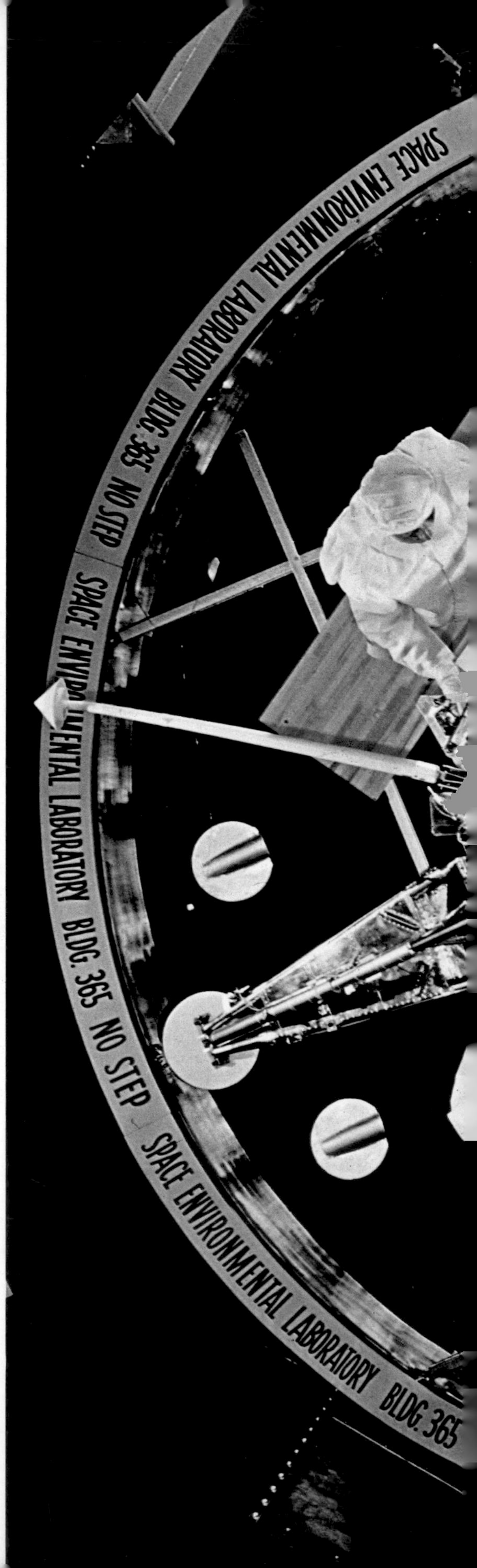

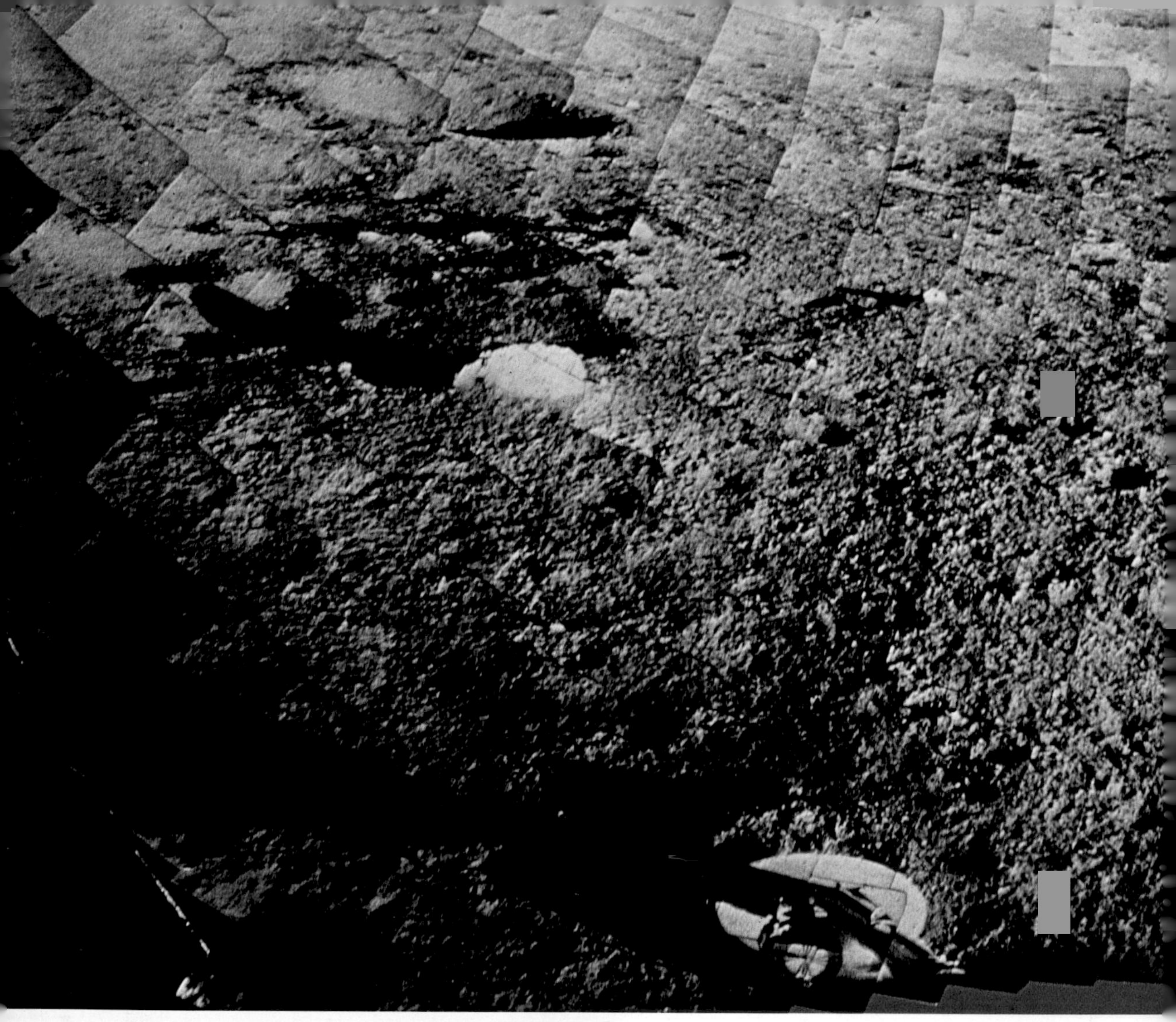

NATIONAL AERONAUTICS AND SPACE ADMINISTRATION

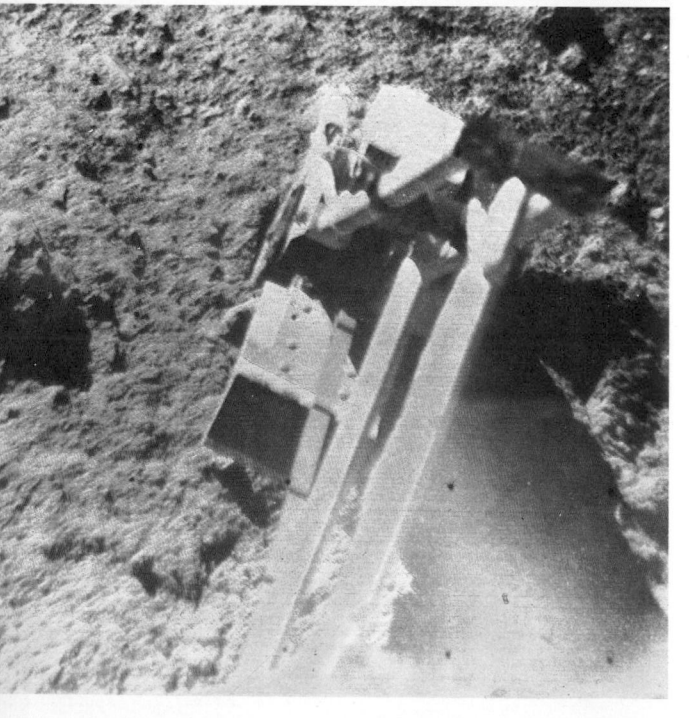

MOSAIC *of photographic chips portrays part of the moon's desolate Ocean of Storms. The horizon lies roughly a mile away. This vista emerged from more than 10,000 images televised by Surveyor I in June, 1966. Surveyor VII (left), its scoop door open, pushes a blade into the lunar surface in January, 1968, to determine the resistance of the soil.*

17 minutes were the first finely detailed pictures of the moon's surface. Run on film like a movie, they gave a remarkably realistic illusion of an impending crash. When the film was later shown to the astronauts in Houston, fun-loving Wally Schirra broke up the house by shouting, when impact seemed imminent, "Bail out, you fool!"

The next epochal stage in lunar photography began in 1966 with soft-landings on the moon of packages containing cameras and other instruments by both the United States and the U.S.S.R. Earlier, on October 4, 1959, scientists of the Soviet

COLOR DISK attached to a foot pad of Surveyor III contrasts with a sample of moon soil deposited by the craft's digging scoop. Scientists on earth used an identical wheel for color comparison to determine that Surveyor pictures shot through orange, green, and blue filters, would, when combined, reveal moon color with reasonable accuracy.

Union had succeeded in photographing the moon's far side with their Luna III probe, but the poor resolution and quality of the pictures greatly limited their value to science.

A soft lunar landing was not an easy undertaking. The problem facing scientists of both countries was formidable: Fire the braking rockets of an incoming lunar probe too soon and the spacecraft would stall too high and fall too hard for its instruments to survive; slow it down too late and it would shatter its electronic brains in a high-velocity crash.

NATIONAL AERONAUTICS AND SPACE ADMINISTRATION (ABOVE); J. R. EYERMAN

On February 3, 1966, the Russians finally succeeded in this delicate braking maneuver. Luna IX, a spherical automatic station weighing about 220 pounds, came safely to rest in the Ocean of Storms. Because lunar gravity is but one-sixth that of earth's, the capsule and its instruments totaled only some 37 pounds on the moon. A radio command from the Soviet ground station opened the lens of Luna IX's TV camera, and the resulting panel of some nine pictures initiated the era of on-the-surface scientific investigation of the moon.

Unknown to the Russians, British scientists had borrowed a telephoto facsimile machine from a newspaper and joined it to their radio telescope at Jodrell Bank in Cheshire. They then tuned to 183 megacycles, the frequency announced by the Russians. When this hasty improvisation worked, the British actually released the pictures to the world before the astonished Russians did.

Then an extraordinary thing happened. When Luna IX pictures started coming in on Saturday morning, February 5, it was obvious from a shift in the horizon angle that Luna IX had moved or lurched during the earth night. Was this evidence of a lunar quake? Was the moon still volcanic? Or did meteoroid impacts cause the camera to change position slightly? No one knew for sure. Later, shortly after I arrived in Russia, I asked Academician Alexander Lebedinsky of the Moscow Planetarium what had happened. He could only speculate that the lurch was due to a breakdown of the soil under the weight of the capsule.

Three and a half months after Luna IX soft-landed, the United States' Surveyor I gently settled its 600 pounds in the vast Ocean of Storms. By now, both countries had also succeeded in placing

MOON-BOUND LASER BEAM *spears into the optical tunnel of the solar telescope at Kitt Peak National Observatory (right) near Tucson, Arizona. A mirror atop the building (left) reflects a narrow, highly concentrated shaft of light toward the moon, blurred during a time exposure. Surveyor VII, photographing the crescent earth (left, above) caught an oncoming beam (circled) from Kitt Peak along with another sent from the Table Mountain Observatory near Wrightwood, California. Astronauts expect to place reflectors on the moon that will bounce back pulsating laser beams. By timing the round trip of the signals, scientists could determine earth-moon distances to within six inches.*

cameras in lunar orbit—the United States with its Lunar Orbiter Series (containing a 150-pound radio-controlled, wide-angle, telephoto-lens camera), and the Soviet Union with a continuation of its orbiting series that began in April, 1966, with Luna X.

By early 1968, clear and usable Ranger, Surveyor, and Lunar Orbiter photographs totaled more than 100,000. Additionally, the Surveyor spacecraft had carried out moon-surface exploration of five areas previously chosen as possible landing sites for the manned Apollo Lunar Module.

"For fifty years," Dr. Shoemaker told me, "man has been speculating about the nature of the lunar surface. Now, thanks primarily to these photographs, we know that at least 99 percent of the surface is composed of fragmented debris. We know its approximate thickness, its bearing strength, its grain-sized texture, and its cohesion. Surveyor told us the basic chemical composition of the lunar plain is basaltic like that of the most common lavas of earth. Scientists are now in 90 percent agreement that the surface fragments are

ORIGINALLY SCHEDULED TO PILOT *the first manned Apollo spacecraft, Astronauts Virgil I. Grissom, Roger B. Chaffee, and Edward White died inside their command capsule when fire broke out during a pre-flight test on January 27, 1967. Nine months later, an automatic camera aboard a similar, unmanned craft, Apollo 4, photographed the earth from more than 11,000 miles high; swirling clouds (left, center) obscure the South Atlantic Ocean.*

NATIONAL AERONAUTICS AND SPACE ADMINISTRATION

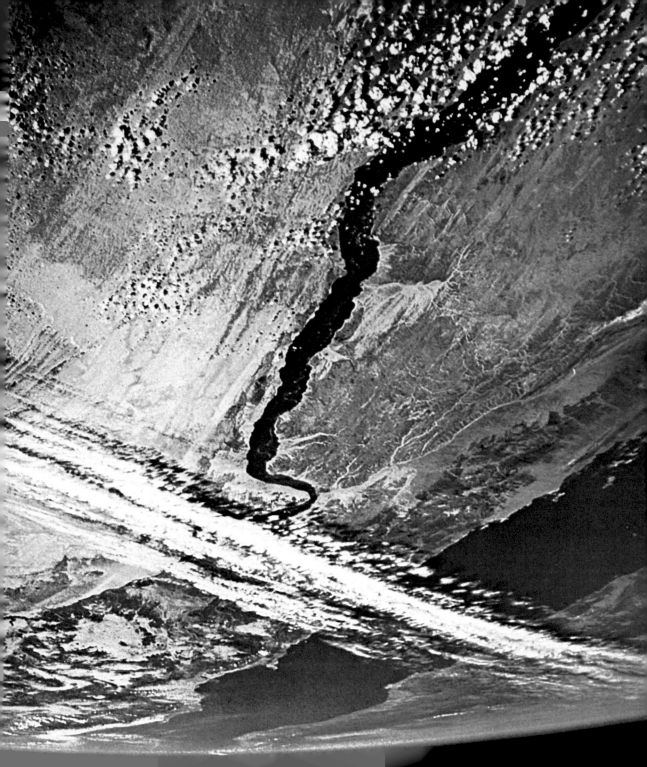

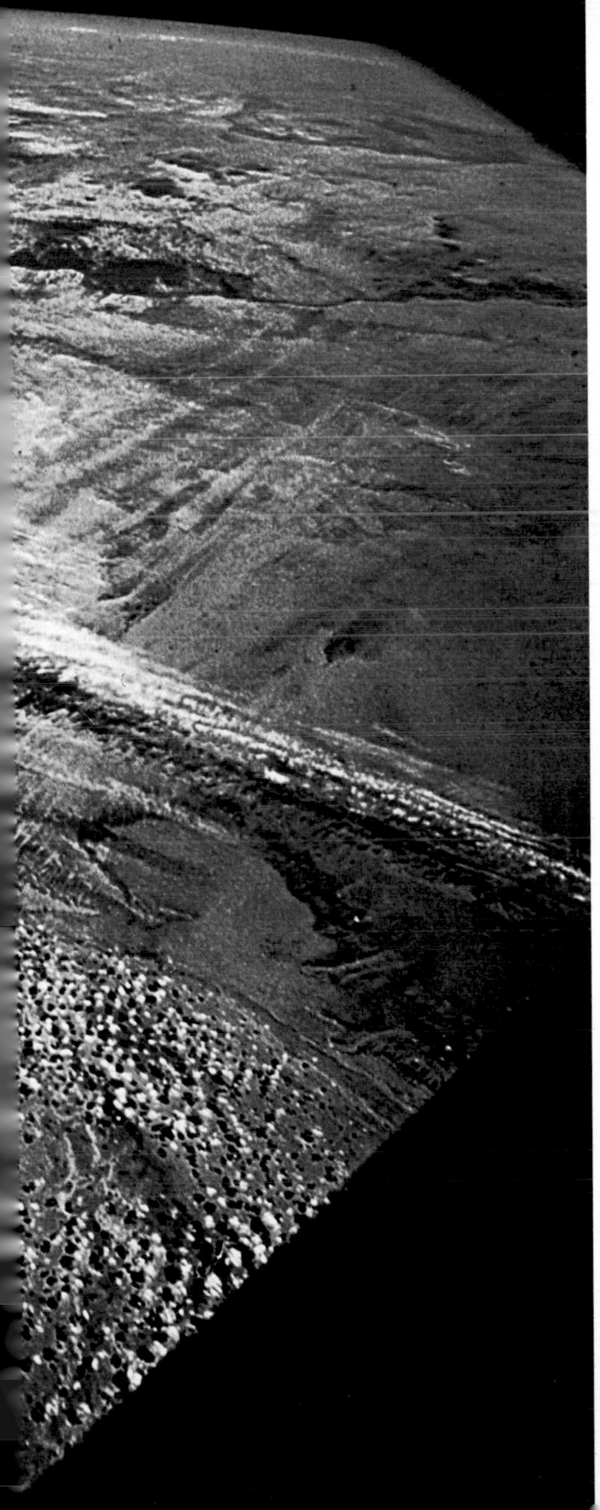

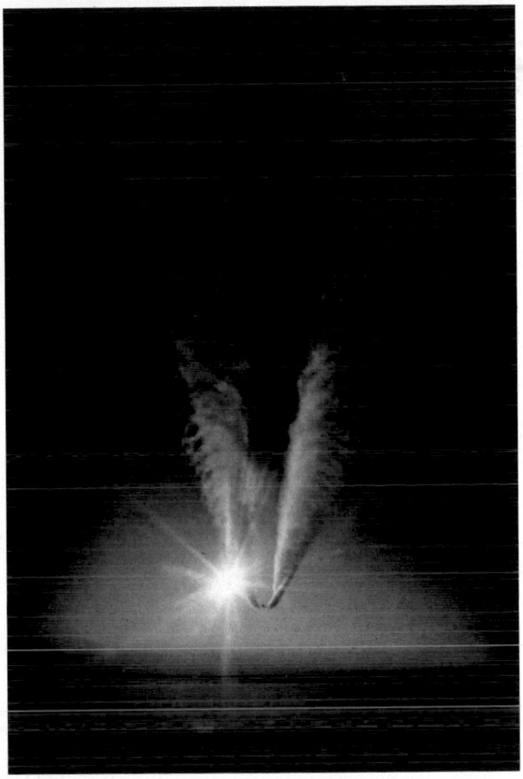

JET STREAMS: RIVERS
OF WIND HIGH OVERHEAD

Streamers of cirrus clouds, caught in a jet stream above Egypt, race across the Nile and the Red Sea in a photograph from the Gemini 12 mission. Born of colliding warm and cold air masses, jet streams circle the globe from west to east, sometimes at 300 miles an hour. Often their force speeds storms along the surface of the earth. The ribbons of wind, as much as 300 miles wide and only four miles deep, occur near the base of the stratosphere at altitudes ranging from 20,000 to 40,000 feet. Ordinarily invisible, jet streams become apparent to the eye only when they create disturbances in high-altitude clouds. B-29 Superfortress pilots, first to fly regularly at 30,000 feet, discovered jet streams during World War II. Flying missions against Japan, they sometimes had to turn back because of powerful head winds. A plane (above), contrails streaming from its engines, flies into the sun as it climbs toward a jet stream. By riding with it, the pilot can save fuel and increase his air speed.

JAMES A. LOVELL, JR., NASA (LEFT); N.G.S. PHOTOGRAPHER BRUCE DALE

NATIONAL GEOGRAPHIC PHOTOGRAPHER ROBERT F. SISSON

WHITE IN THE SUN'S GLARE, *a large eddy carrying young pink shrimp toward their nursery grounds in the Bay of Florida, swirls lazily beneath Gemini 4, orbiting 138 miles overhead. Florida shrimp fishermen annually catch 15 to 20 million pounds of* Penaeus duorarum *in this area. Biologists have learned from such photographs that young shrimp enter the bay on currents through the passageways between the Florida Keys. Spawned in deep water in the Gulf of Mexico (below), baby shrimp hitch rides on eddies and tides to the sand bars and reefs between the mainland and the Keys. Many drift into the Everglades. They remain five to seven months. Halfgrown, they head back to deep water, and after spawning spend the balance of their lives there. Florida fishing boats, like the* Miss Fleta *(left), net the creatures at night, when they rise from their daytime beds in the seafloor mud.*

GULF OF MEXICO   FLORIDA MAINLAND

SHRIMP SPAWN AT 60 TO 240 FEET OR MORE

LIFE CYCLE OF THE PINK SHRIMP

EGGS   FLOOR OF GULF

the cumulative end product of prolonged meteoroid bombardment of the moon.''

Since the beginning of the Space Age, photography has become one of the scientist's most important means of gathering and preserving information. Houston's Manned Spacecraft Center provided astronauts training in terrain and weather photography and gave them extensive practice in using the Hasselblad 500C, the Maurer 77mm Space Camera and the other photographic equipment adapted for use in space. So demanding were photographic duties in orbit that most astronauts heartily sympathized with Gordon Cooper, who made the first comprehensive photographic study of the earth's ''night glow'' during his flight in *Faith 7*. After taking pictures, as he put it, ''all night long,'' Cooper drawled from space, ''. . . all I do is take pictures, pictures, pictures.''

Astronaut attention to photography, however, has produced a near-incredible record of the first

period in history in which man could see his planet recorded from space. Their views of the continents, the panoramic sweep of the seas, and, above all, their capture of the full range of world weather—from serenely placid to darkly ominous—comprise an unprecedented scientific and esthetic treasury.

In combination with photographs taken from such automatic earth satellites as Nimbus and ESSA, the colorfully captured record of our planet's surface is already bringing economic benefits. Geologists use the photographs to prospect for oil and other minerals, to study erosion along coastlines, and to detect changes in the courses of rivers. Oceanographers use them not only in studies of marine biology and fish migration but also to investigate the way ocean currents erode the floor of the sea.

Turning their cameras away from earth, scientists sent moving platforms millions of miles into

EDWARD H. WHITE II, GEMINI 4, NASA

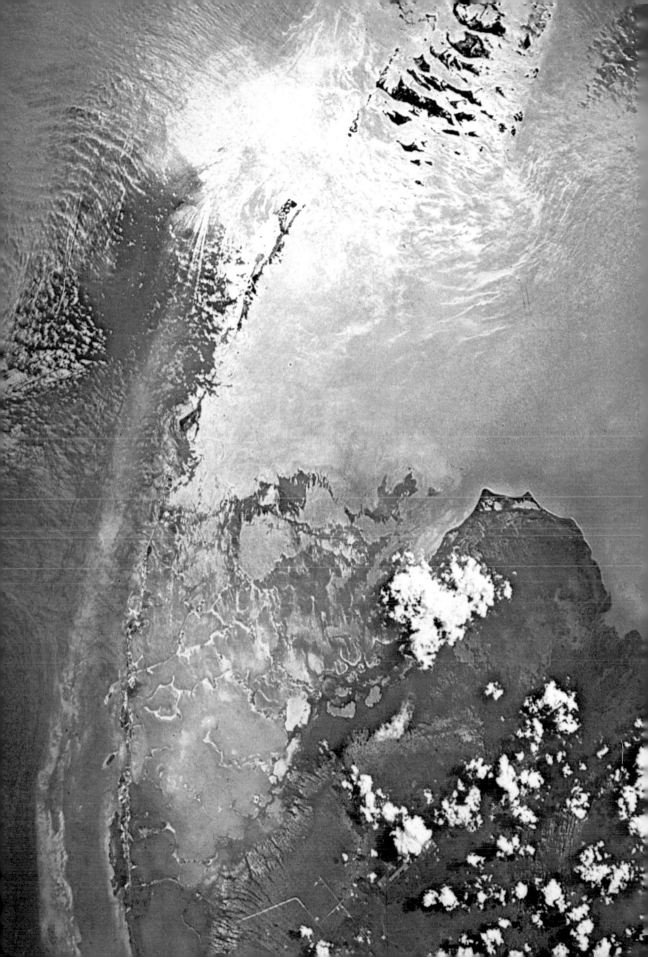

CHARLES CONRAD, NASA

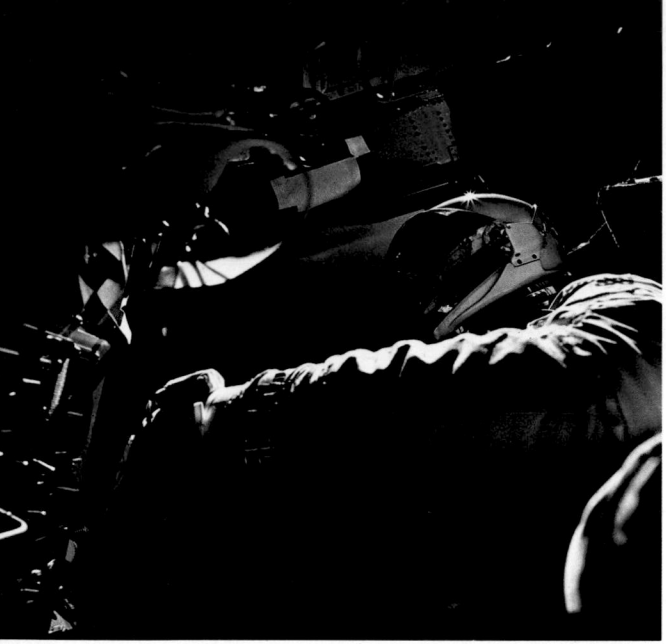

GEMINI 11 HATCH *open, Astronaut Richard F. Gordon, Jr., jettisons a clutter of tethering gear used on the rendezvous and docking mission he flew with Charles Conrad, Jr., in September, 1966. Algeria's 1,500-foot-high Tifernine sand dunes (right) appeared 150 miles below Gemini 7 Astronauts Frank Borman and James A. Lovell, Jr., in December, 1965. Command Pilot Borman took the picture with a hand-held Hasselblad camera; the scattering effect of the atmosphere tinted the earth blue.*

space to photograph the sun and to capture dramatic closeup views of Martian craters. Automatic and manually operated cameras recorded vistas, unhampered by the volatile atmosphere of earth, where swirls distort the view of both eye and lens. From space, as Cooper put it, lights on earth twinkle; it is the stars that remain steady and unblinking.

It is this outward view that many scientists feel is ultimately the most valid reason for sending photographic recorders beyond the atmosphere. For much of what man himself will eventually see as he ventures deeper into space, he will first see on film. And whether that clear distant image falls on cameras and spectrographs in earth orbit or on semi-permanent instruments implanted to gaze outward from the far side of the moon, that image is certain to give man simultaneously both knowledge and the incentive to reach for knowledge. For good pictures show us not only where we have been, but also where we are going.

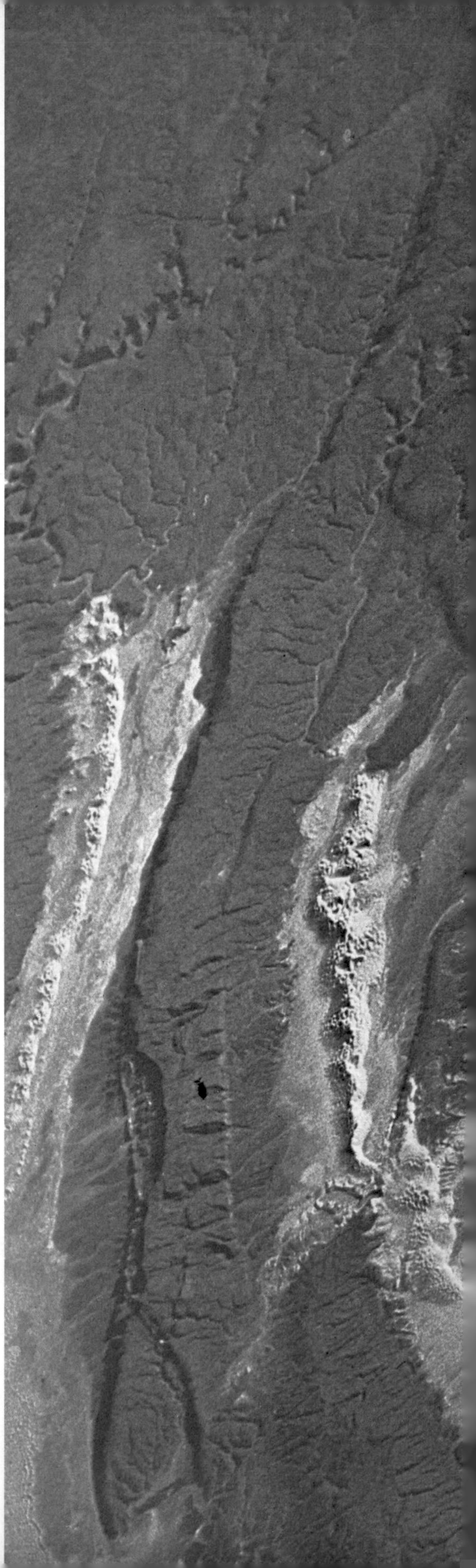

FRANK BORMAN, NASA

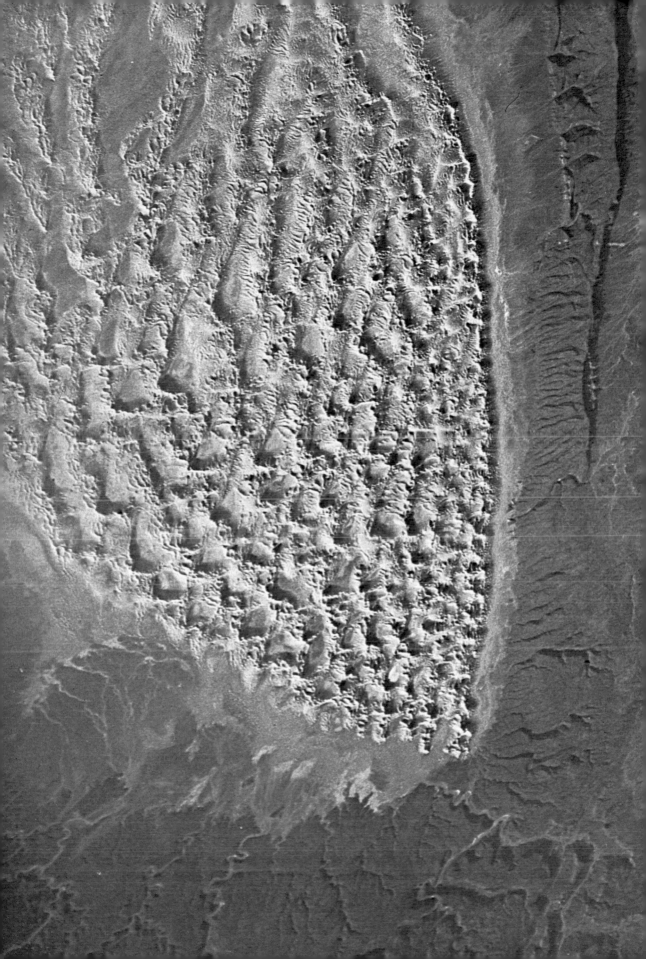

7 / REACHING FOR THE MOON: CULMINATION OF A DREAM

Sleep in lunar orbit? On the very doorstep of the moon? Shades of Jules Verne!

Will man — at such a moment — really be able to close his eyes and nod and drift in earthly slumber?

A difficult assignment indeed, but NASA's reasoning on this point is convincing. After three busy, keyed-up days en route, the two astronauts chosen to go down to the crater-pocked lunar surface will have but 26 hours in which to carry out an exacting series of tasks. To be able to sleep beforehand, if only briefly, will help prepare them for their greatest test yet.

This decision is only one of millions NASA has had to make in preparing for the voyage that someday soon will bridge the 240,000-mile space chasm that separates earth from its moon. To picture man about to set foot on the lunar surface is no longer a mere dream.

For the United States and for the Soviet Union, lunar exploration ranks as an epic milestone along the great, uncharted highways of space. On the way, the two nations already have climbed a hundred Everests. Even to begin to turn dream into reality, they faced two crucial engineering challenges: to perfect a booster train powerful enough to propel a 50-ton payload to the moon and to develop a space ship that would function as a home and vehicle for man during the trip to the moon and back.

Secondary challenges were no less difficult: perfecting computer-controlled guidance and navigation accurate enough to land the moon ship on an invisible lunar runway; mastering the technique of entering and leaving both earth and lunar orbits, of rendezvousing and docking with another object in space, and of re-entering the near-earth atmosphere; designing a space suit to protect and sustain a man and permit him to work both inside and outside his ship; overcoming the problems of moving and working in the weightlessness of space as well as in the one-sixth earth gravity astronauts will confront on the moon; setting up worldwide communications; perfecting spacecraft recovery

INSIDE AN ATLAS *rocket propellant tank of bright stainless steel, General Dynamics technicians in San Diego, California, install baffles to prevent the liquid from sloshing. At lift-off, the rocket carries 300,000 pounds of propellants. The Atlas lofted Mercury astronauts on all their orbital flights.*

CONVAIR DIVISION, GENERAL DYNAMICS

MERCURY ASTRONAUT *John Glenn clambers gingerly into* Friendship 7 *as technicians run a final check before lift-off from Cape Canaveral in 1962. Orbital sunset gilds his face in a photograph made by an automatic camera during America's first earth-girdling mission. Dr. William K. Douglas, the astronauts' physician, waits silently during the tense moments of re-entry. A malfunction resulted in the fiery disintegration of the retrorocket pack, and led Glenn to exclaim, "... that was a real fireball, boy!"*

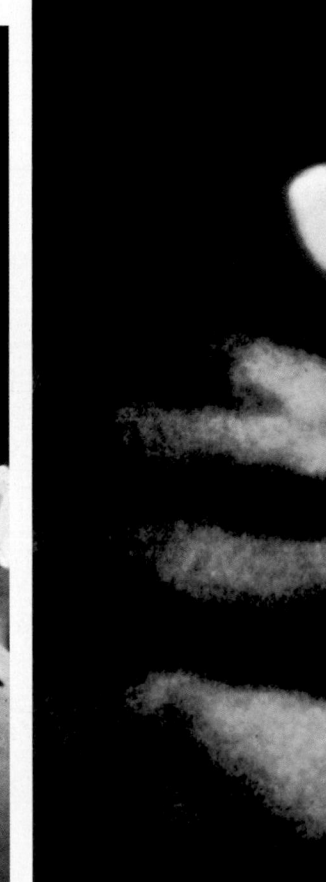

NASA (ABOVE RIGHT) AND BILL TAUB, NASA

techniques; developing ways to handle food required by the body; and, finally, solving the myriad details required in the operation and housekeeping of a spacecraft.

Space engineers had to find new structures and materials to withstand unprecedented shocks and vibrations. They had to develop and test new metals, alloys, and synthetics to sustain the extreme heat — up to 5,970° F. — in rocket-engine combustion chambers. To protect the outside of a spacecraft during the searing heat of re-entry, they had to design insulation able to handle temperatures above 4,000° F. To power monstrous boosters they

had to learn about new rocket propellants—how to make them, transport them, store them, load them, control them, and burn them efficiently.

Finally, program administrators of both the U.S.S.R. and the United States had to prepare the greatest variable of all—man himself, at once the weakest and strongest link in the mastery of space. Astronauts and cosmonauts had to attend courses in astrophysics, propulsion, astronomy, geology, and dozens of other subjects. They also studied every component and system of the booster and vehicle. They spent hour upon hour in mission simulators of remarkable ingenuity and week after

week on field trips, in rigorous physical conditioning, and in survival training.

Both countries worked out major solutions in stages—and in amazingly parallel time periods. Gagarin opened the first phase, the one-man flights, on April 12, 1961—a date now commemorated as Cosmonaut Day in the Soviet Union. With the suborbital flight of Alan Shepard in *Freedom 7* just days away, the shy young Russian became the first of the new instant-heroes of space, proving that man could perform comfortably and efficiently in space, at least for one orbit. The Vostok 1 flight, along with Shepard's Mercury flight

23 days later, also proved that man was on the right track in the concepts of booster and spacecraft design and guidance and re-entry procedures. The six Vostok and six Mercury flights gradually extended these basic achievements through longer and longer periods.

The U. S. launching of John Glenn into three orbits presented people everywhere with a unique human and engineering triumph. First, Glenn's automatic attitude control system lost two of its thrusters, and he had to assume manual control of *Friendship 7.* Then instruments indicated his heat shield, the protective saucer designed to boil off the heat of re-entry, had torn loose. If truly ajar, the shield might be dislodged by the buffeting atmosphere, and Glenn could be incinerated.

Mission officials decided to leave on the projecting retrorockets after firing, in the belief that the metal straps securing the braking package also would hold the vital heat shield in place. While millions held their breath, John Glenn plummeted in radio silence into the harsh crucible of the near-earth atmosphere. Great flaming chunks of metal, melted by the intense heat, tore loose from the protruding retropackage.

Then Glenn suddenly exclaimed, "My condition is good, but that was a real fireball, boy!" and the world sighed in relief.

More directly related to the moon mission were the two- and three-man flights that began in late 1964. The opening three-man flight of Voskhod 1 discarded the use of space suits, indicating a progression to more reliable space ships. With a physician aboard, the flight returned an enormous amount of biomedical data and, for the first time, tested braking rockets for cushioning the landing.

The first manned Gemini flight of Gus Grissom and John Young established that orbital maneuvers were possible, and the twin space-walk flights of the United States and the U.S.S.R.—a mere 11 weeks apart—demonstrated conclusively that man could venture from his space home.

To judge by the space walkers' reactions, "walking" or "swimming" in space was an almost intoxicating experience. Cosmonaut Alexei Leonov later commented, "The boundless expanses of outer space unfolded before me in their indescribable beauty. . . . I felt fine, was in excellent spirits and did not want to part with free space."

Ed White overextended his stay outside Gemini by eight minutes. Finally, fellow Astronaut James McDivitt relayed an order from Houston's Mission Control Center:

"They want you to come back in now."

"This is fun," White replied.

"Well, back in. Come on."

"I'm coming."

"O.K. Whoops, take it easy now."

"Aren't you going to hold my hand?"

"No, come on in here."

"It's the saddest moment of my life," White said, with the reluctance of a country boy forsaking a cool creek.

(Continued on page 155)

BILL TAUB, NASA

SURGICALLY CLEAN *white room encloses the Gemini 4 spacecraft, in place atop its 90-foot Titan II rocket, before launch on June 3, 1965. The 25-foot-square compartment, here photographed through a Fisheye lens, serves as a workshop for engineers and technicians and a boarding platform for astronauts. At T-minus-35-minutes, hydraulic engines lower the white room, freeing the rocket for lift-off. At right, Command Pilot James McDivitt, foreground, and space-walker Ed White recline in the craft before sealing the hatch.*

JAMES A. McDIVITT, NASA (ABOVE AND OPPOSITE)

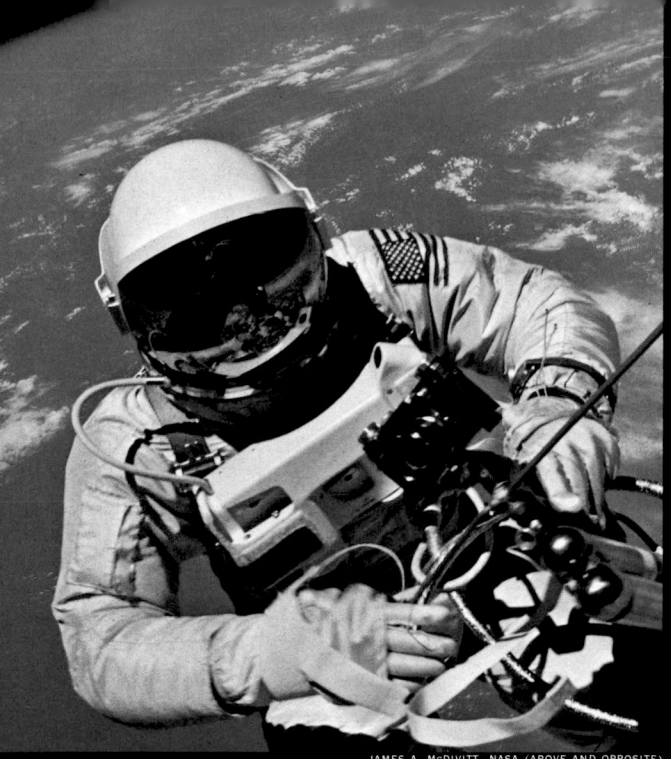

Floating in space 100 miles up, Major White moves freely during his 20-minute venture from Gemini 4. Tethered by a 25-foot umbilical cord containing oxygen and communication lines, the astronaut maneuvered by releasing compressed oxygen from a hand-held propulsion gun. Although he traveled some 6,000 miles outside the space capsule at 17,500 miles an hour, White said he "had little sensation of speed and no sensation of falling."

FROM 16MM SEQUENCE CAMERA, NASA

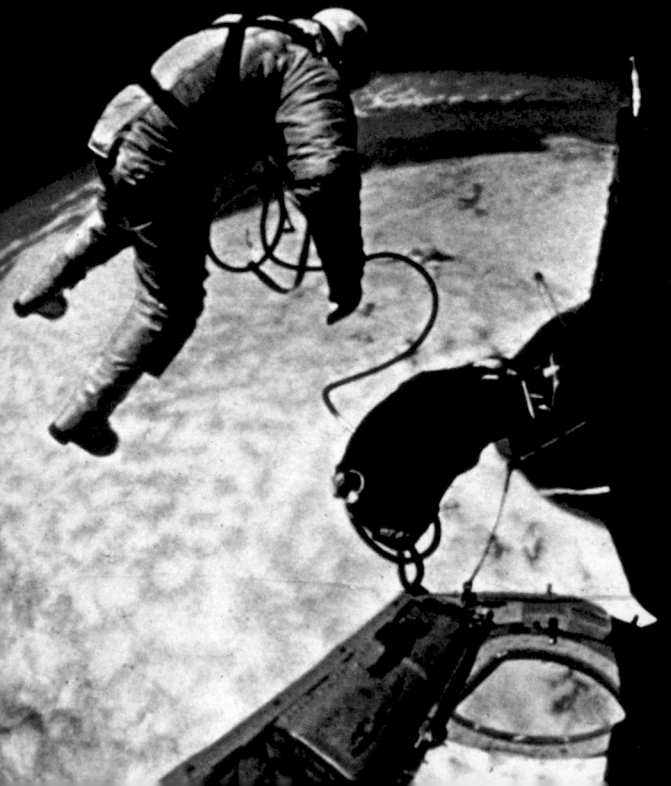

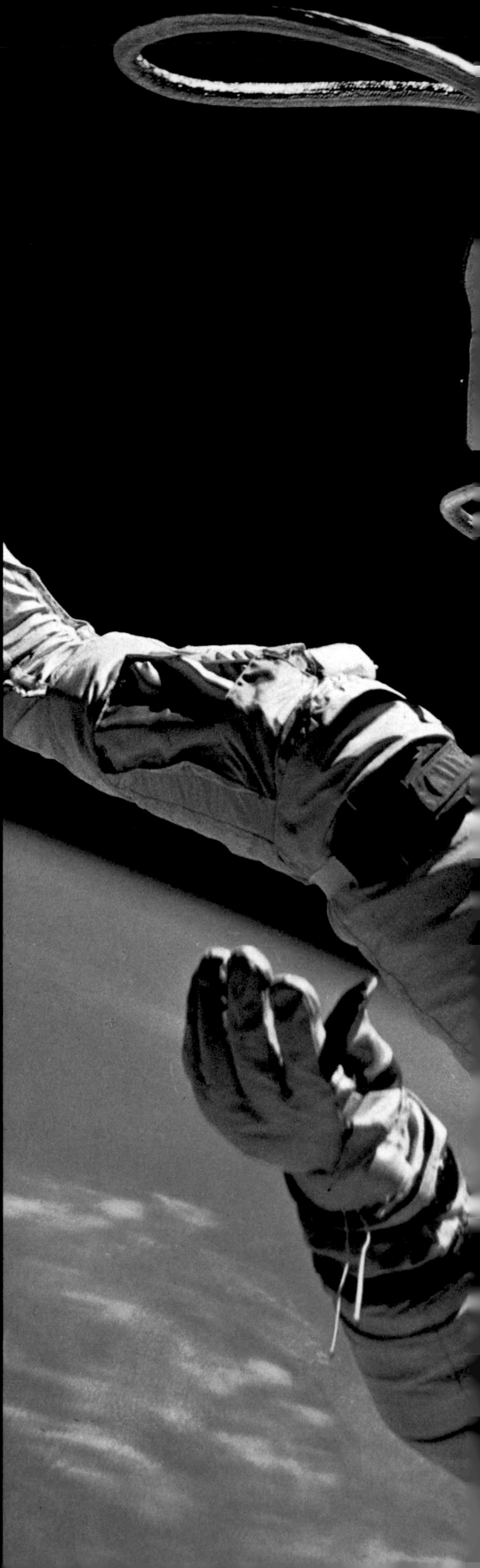

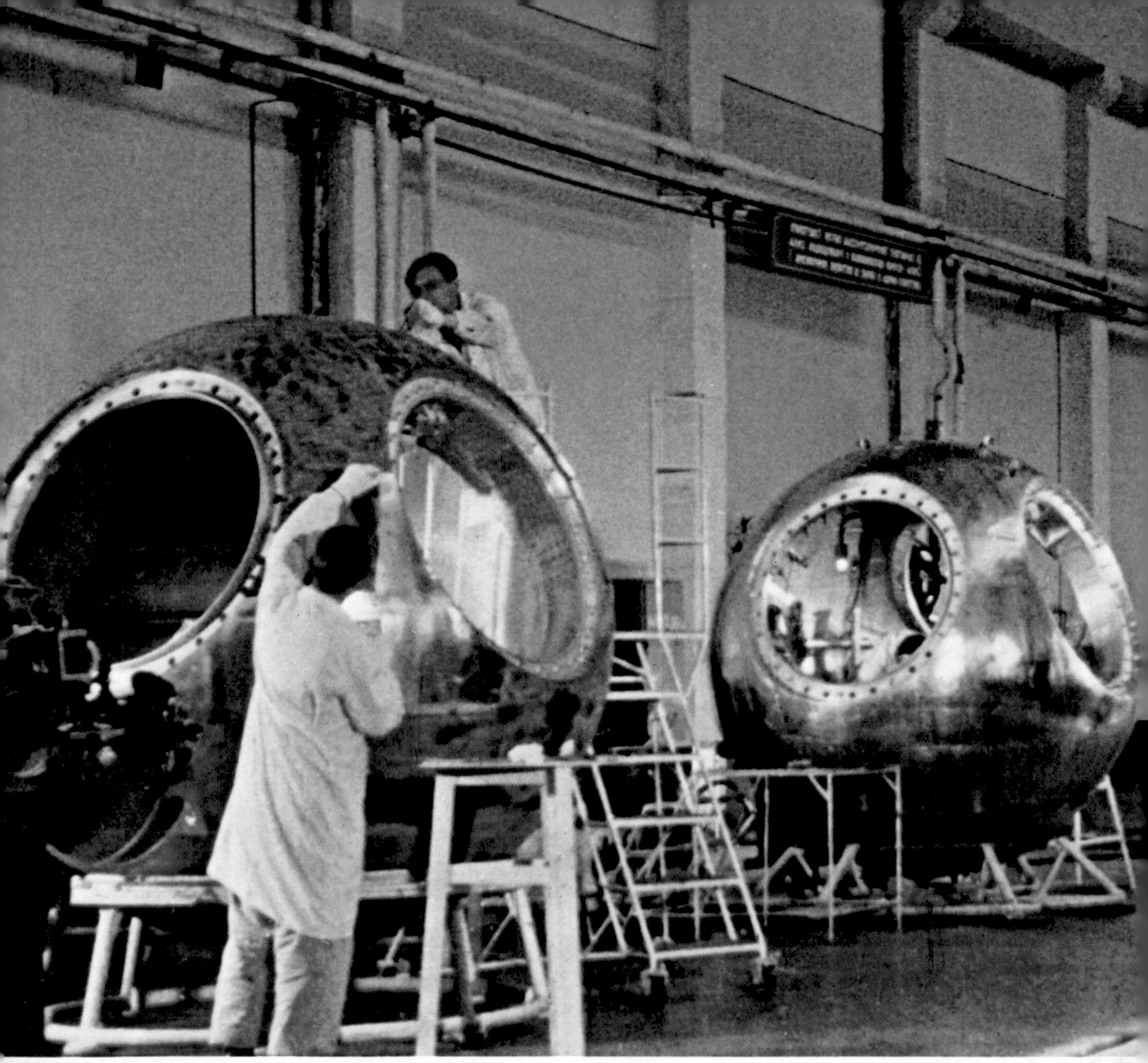

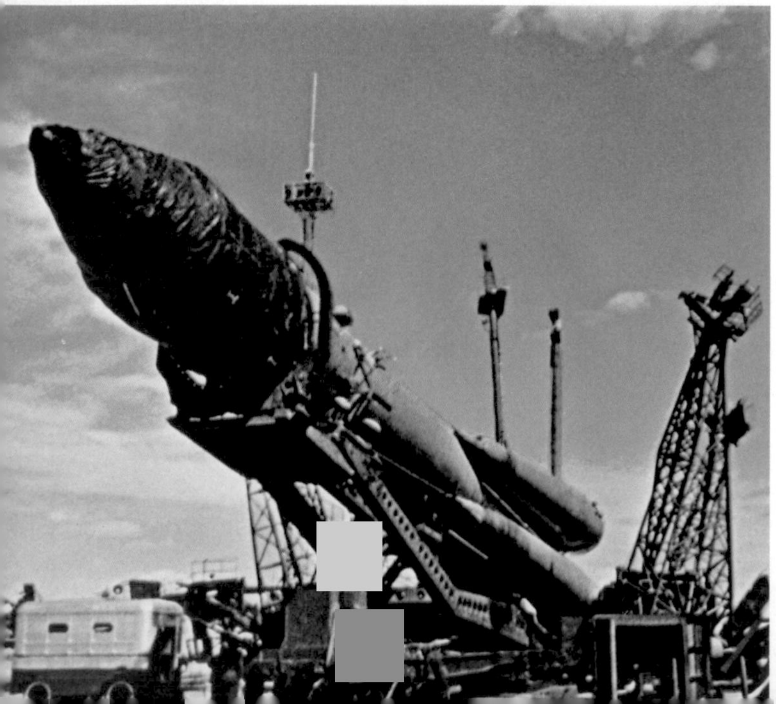

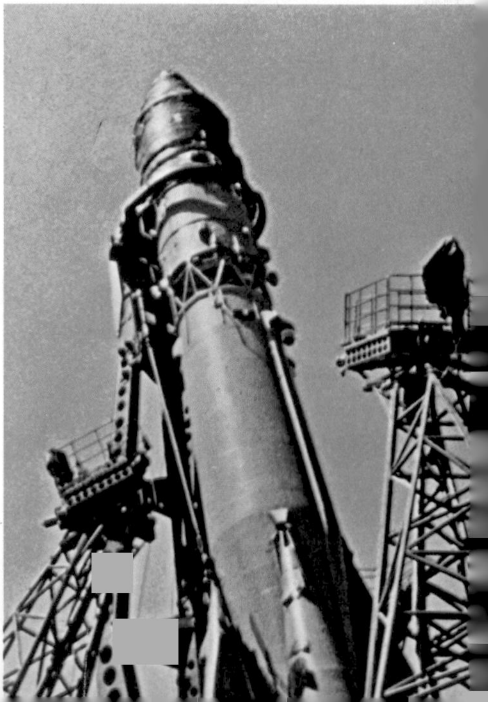

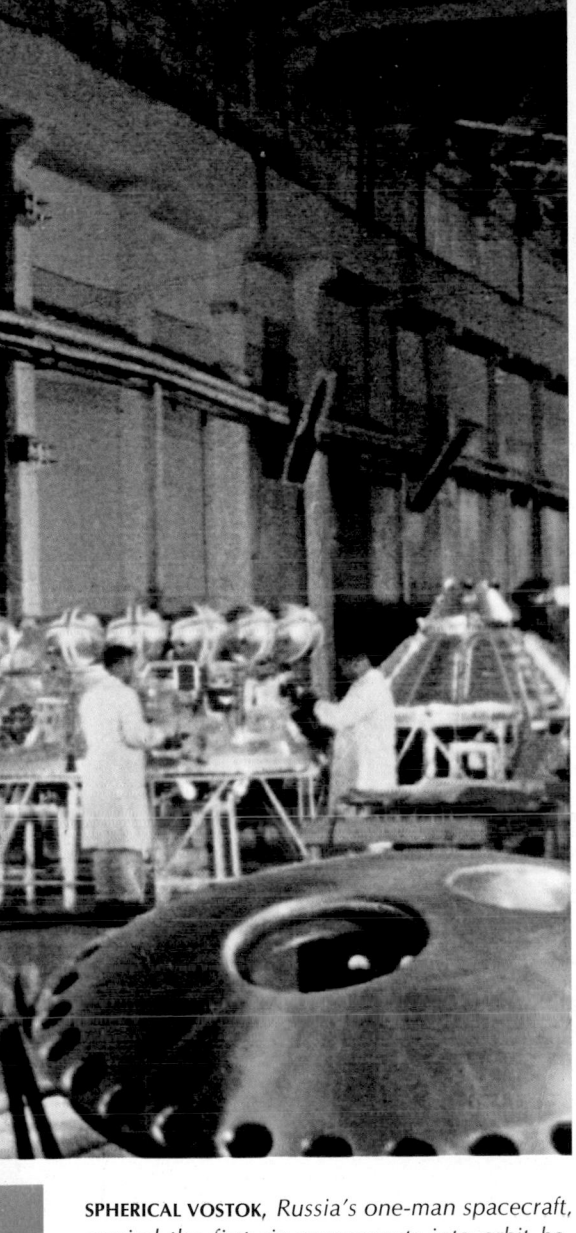

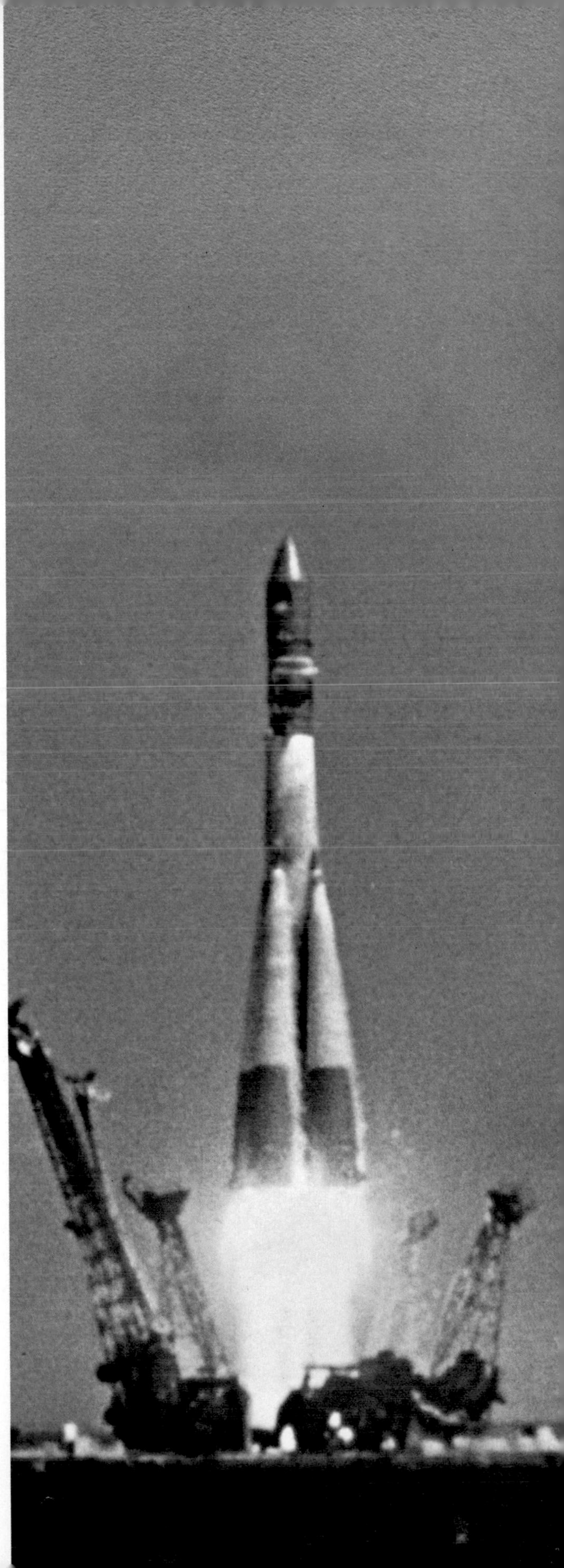

SPHERICAL VOSTOK, *Russia's one-man spacecraft, carried the first six cosmonauts into orbit between 1961 and 1963. In a Soviet factory, technicians assemble two of the 2½-ton, eight-foot-wide capsules. An escape hatch rests nearby. The Russians built and tested the entire rocket in a horizontal position, rolling it out to the launch area, then winching it upright. A rail-borne lifter begins raising the Vostok rocket (opposite, left). As it nears the vertical, sway braces from the launch platform grasp the rocket and hold it in place. At lift-off from the Baykonur launch pad in southern Russia, the braces fall away. A three-stage Vostok similar to this carried Maj. Yuri Gagarin into space.*

SOVFOTO (ABOVE AND RIGHT) AND NOVOSTI

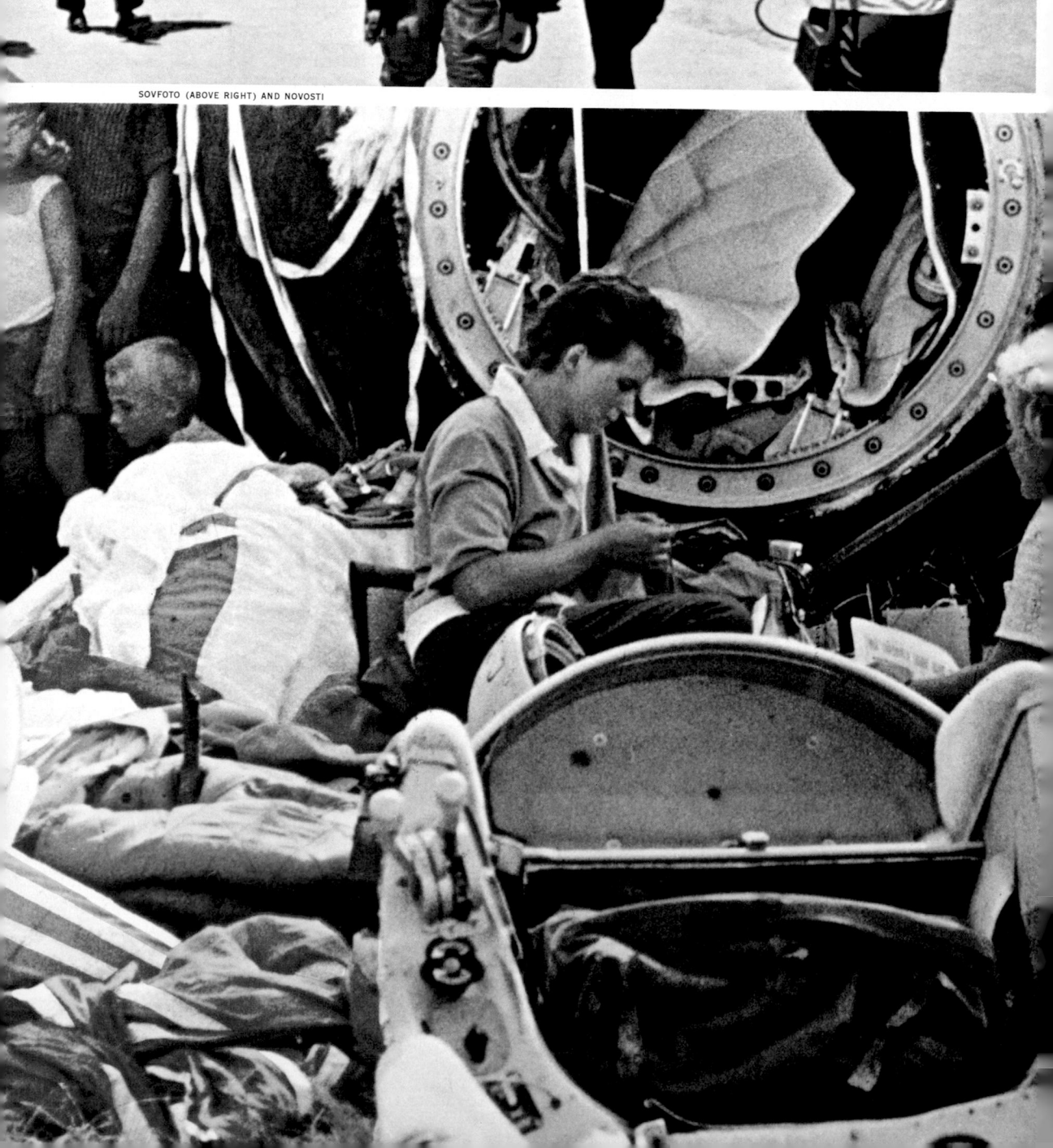

SOVFOTO (ABOVE RIGHT) AND NOVOSTI

After Colonel Leonov's emergence into the space vacuum, a lapse in Russian manned flights began that was to last for more than two years. Gemini, in the meantime, surged through a series of brilliant engineering triumphs in the remainder of a 12-flight series—ten of them manned.

In Gemini 5, my neighbor Gordon Cooper and Pete Conrad tried out a vital forerunner of future flights—the use of a fuel cell to provide electricity and water from a combination of hydrogen and oxygen. The prototype fuel cell did not perform as planned, but engineers were able to build a better power unit based directly on the experience of the flight.

In Gemini 6-A, veteran Astronaut Wally Schirra and copilot Thomas Stafford drew the challenge of attempting a rendezvous with Frank Borman and Jim Lovell in Gemini 7. Earlier, Jim McDivitt had been scheduled to attempt a rendezvous with the Titan second stage that went into orbit with him. While he was busy with an alignment maneuver, the rocket began to drift out of sight; residual fuel venting from its tanks apparently had given the target a mind of its own.

"The booster fell away pretty rapidly . . ." he reported to the ground. "I have been struggling here not to let it get too far from me."

Eventually darkness forced a cancellation of additional tries at a rendezvous, denying U. S. astronauts their first practical lesson in coping with the upside-down laws of orbital mechanics. To catch up with the elusive booster, McDivitt knew he would have to go against all his earth-bound instincts and "put on the brakes." Braking would, in effect, speed him up—dropping his spacecraft into a lower, and faster, orbit. Were he to thrust forward, he would rise into a higher, but slower, orbit.

Schirra, entering a faster, "inside-track" orbit

1,200 miles behind Gemini 7, began the series of delicate maneuvers that were to mark the historic 100,000-mile chase through space. As computers in Houston and aboard Gemini 6-A reconciled speeds and relative positions into usable factors of direction and thrust, he skillfully timed his burns to catch up, at the same time climbing slowly toward Gemini 7's orbit. Still 439 miles behind, Schirra turned his ship at a right angle to its line of flight and fired his aft thrusters for 40 seconds to jockey Gemini 6-A into Gemini 7's orbital plane.

Slowly the gap closed. Edging toward Gemini 7, Schirra alerted ground controllers in Hawaii, "There seems to be a lot of traffic up here." Finally, 5 hours and 56 minutes after launch, Gemini 6-A nosed to within 120 feet of its sister ship—and 2 hours later—to within a single foot.

On the next flight, Astronauts Neil Armstrong and David Scott took an additional vital step. After rendezvous with an unmanned Agena target vehicle, Gemini 8 smoothly inserted its nose into Agena's docking cone; automatic latches securely locked the two together.

"Like parking a car," Armstrong said, describing the docking. But 27 minutes later, a short-circuited Gemini thruster put the combination into a dangerous spin, and Armstrong undocked. To regain control of Gemini 8, he had to resort to using his Re-entry Control System, even though this meant an abrupt end to the mission; once the system was activated he had to land as soon as possible.

During later missions, rendezvous and docking took place under more ideal conditions. Astronauts Tom Stafford and Eugene Cernan refined the technique in Gemini 9-A when they achieved rendezvous three times with their target vehicle. Cernan also discovered some human limitations to walking in space when vapor formed over his face plate and obscured his vision, forcing him to return to his ship. John Young and Michael Collins in Gemini 10 not only latched on to the 26-foot Agena target, but they also used its 16,000-pound-thrust engine to boost them into a new record apogee of 476 miles.

During the first orbit of their Gemini 11 flight, Astronauts Pete Conrad and Dick Gordon docked with Agena, then fired its engine for 25 long seconds. By the time they passed above Australia on the other side of the world, they had coasted to a new altitude record of 850 miles. Looping back to a close earth orbit, the free-floating spacecraft picked up speed from the powerful pull of the earth's gravity, and in the process set a new speed record of 17,897 miles per hour.

Gemini 11 also provided an opportunity for another space walk by Gordon and a "station keeping" experiment, when the Gemini spacecraft was attached to Agena by a 100-foot Dacron cord.

The final flight of the series, Gemini 12, became the "catchall." Those experiments most important to the Apollo series went on the schedule, including docking and space-walking—extravehicular activity—by copilot Edwin Aldrin. When Gemini 12 finally splashed down, closing the curtain on

RETRIEVAL CRANE *on the U.S.S.* Wasp *hauls Gemini 6-A out of the Atlantic on December 16, 1965, 630 miles southwest of Bermuda. Astronauts Wally Schirra and Tom Stafford elected to stay in the capsule until lifted aboard the carrier. Green dye marked the spacecraft's location. At left, Navy pararescue men—dropped from helicopters to secure Gemini 11—wait with Richard Gordon, at end of raft, and Charles Conrad after the astronauts' splash-down on September 15, 1966, Minutes later, a helicopter whisked them to the U.S.S.* Guam.

THOMAS P. STAFFORD, NASA

his Nation's prelude to the moon mission, spacecraft commander Jim Lovell had accumulated nearly 18 days in orbit during his two Gemini flights, enough to take him—at Space Age velocities—well over seven million miles.

Side by side with this invaluable flight experience, Project Apollo, soon to overshadow the combined efforts of the Gemini and Mercury series, began to gain form and substance. One decision alone, on the best way to get to the moon, required over a million man-hours of technical study. After day-and-night discussions, American spacemen chose the Lunar Orbit Rendezvous method, rejecting a direct flight to the moon as requiring too large a booster for the return trip.

The Earth Orbital Rendezvous method, requiring two launch vehicles, is the approach favored by the Soviet Union. In planetary probes and in several automatic docking experiments in their Cosmos series, Soviet scientists have become practiced in assembling multiple components in earth orbit. From here a spaceship could head directly toward a moon landing, as Russia did with its unmanned Luna IX, or it could first go into lunar parking orbit, as called for in Project Apollo.

Writing in the NATIONAL GEOGRAPHIC in March, 1964, NASA's Deputy Administrator, Dr. Hugh L. Dryden, explained, "We chose the [Lunar Orbit Rendezvous] method for many complex technical reasons. In essence, however, it seemed safer, less complicated, and represented an important saving in payload weight."

There were delays, however, in the manned lunar missions of both Russia and the U. S.—unpredictable and tragic delays which originated not on the moon, but on earth.

The United States suffered first, on January 27, 1967, when Astronauts Gus Grissom, Ed White, and Roger Chaffee were killed in a disastrous fire while going through a routine checkout of their unchristened Apollo spacecraft atop Cape Kennedy's pad 34. Investigative teams were never able to isolate the precise cause of the fire. They could say only that it was probably of electrical origin. By the time the entire inside of the spacecraft was rebuilt with low-flammability materials, accumulated delays in Project Apollo had mounted to well over a year.

Less than three months after the pad 34 tragedy Cosmonaut Vladimir Komarov was killed when his parachute lines fouled while he was attempting to return to earth after 18 orbits in the Soviet Union's own third-generation spacecraft, Soyus 1.

In Moscow in June of 1966 I had chatted through an interpreter with Colonel Komarov. The cosmonaut had smiling, dark brown eyes and very white teeth. Laughingly, he told me how he had broken his nose playing ice hockey with other cosmonauts. When I gave him a Gemini tie pin as a souvenir, he responded by pinning on my coat a gold and ruby pin from the tunic of his uniform.

But though tragedy forced revisions in the lunar program timetables of both countries, the surging

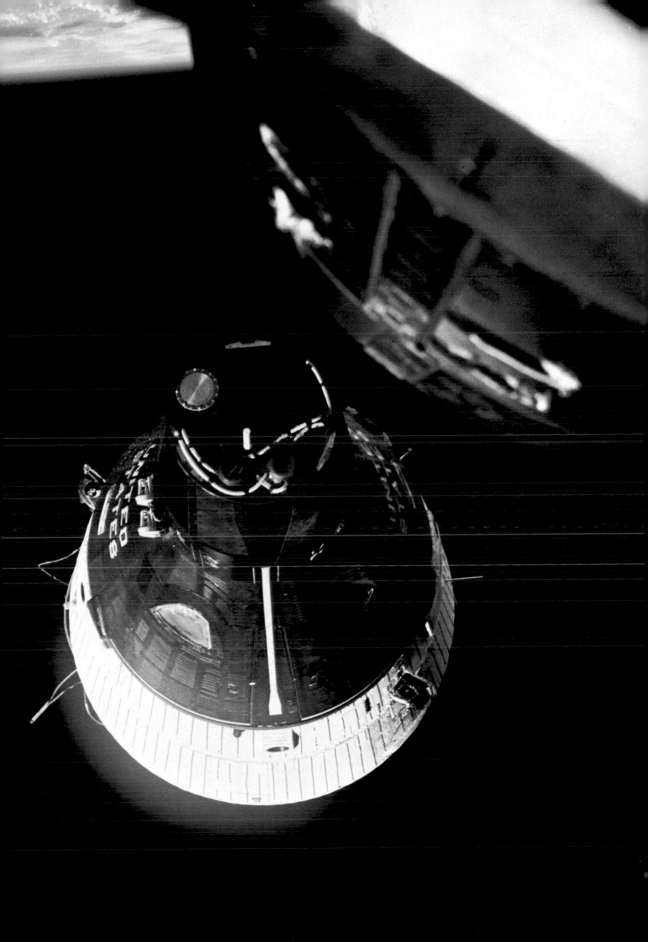

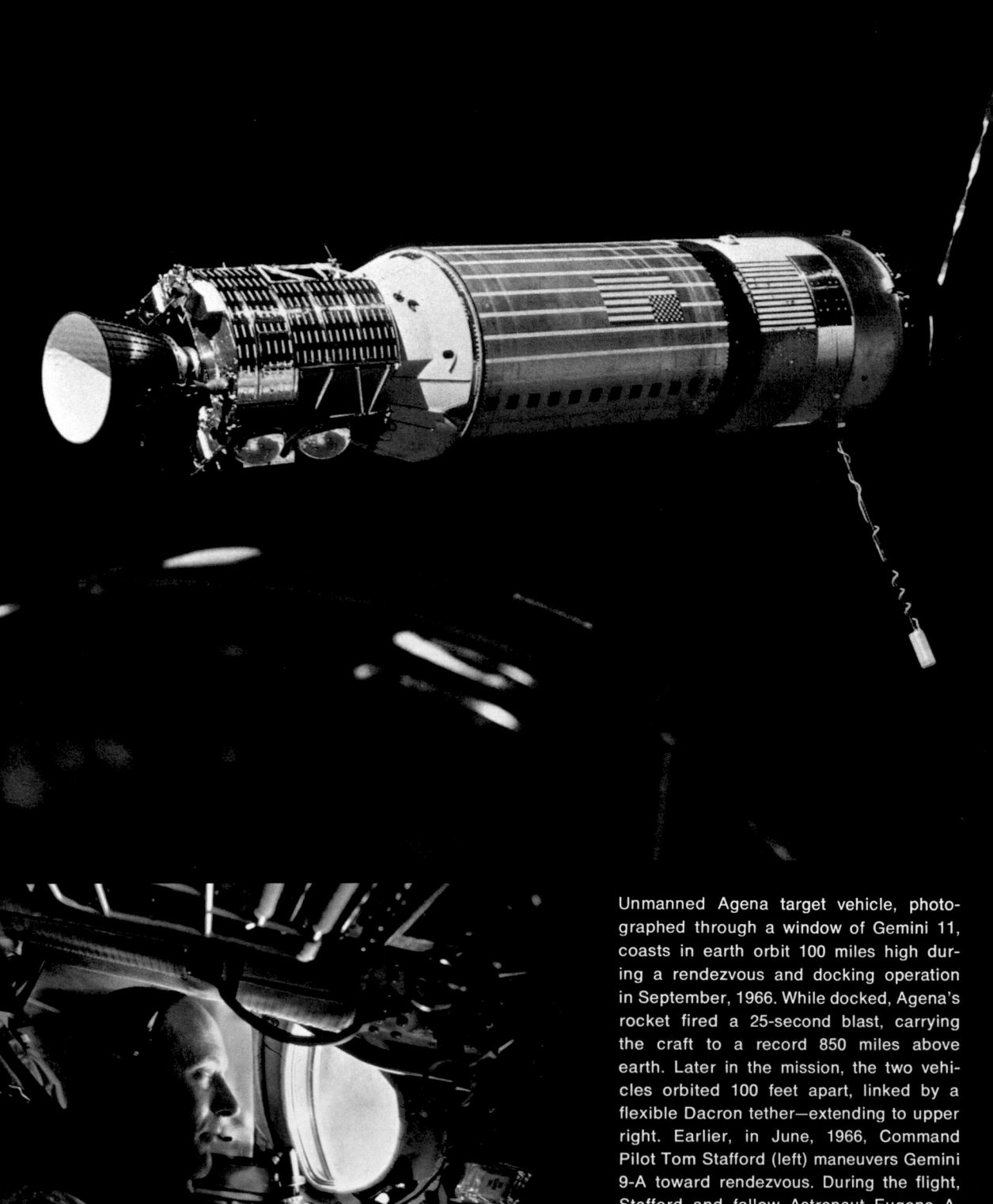

Unmanned Agena target vehicle, photographed through a window of Gemini 11, coasts in earth orbit 100 miles high during a rendezvous and docking operation in September, 1966. While docked, Agena's rocket fired a 25-second blast, carrying the craft to a record 850 miles above earth. Later in the mission, the two vehicles orbited 100 feet apart, linked by a flexible Dacron tether—extending to upper right. Earlier, in June, 1966, Command Pilot Tom Stafford (left) maneuvers Gemini 9-A toward rendezvous. During the flight, Stafford and fellow Astronaut Eugene A. Cernan achieved rendezvous during the third, fourth, and twelfth orbits. The Gemini program, including ten manned flights, provided a testing phase for the manned Apollo lunar landing project.

momentum of the Space Age continued to move us inexorably closer to the moon—ever nearer to the day the gargantuan 3,050-ton Saturn V rocket launches a team of American astronauts toward their first landing on the moon. From the moment the astronauts begin their ascent to their command module atop the mighty space courier, poised on Launch Complex 39 of the John F. Kennedy Space Center on Merritt Island, it will be as if we were following in their footsteps.

Before entering the elevator to ascend to our cabin, we get a close look at Saturn's business end. At the base we see the conical nozzles of the five main-stage engines, fueled by refined kerosene, RP-1, and liquid oxygen, LOX. Together, the engines develop 7.5 million pounds of thrust—more than 20 times that of the Atlas rocket which put John Glenn into orbit in 1962.

We must rise 12 stories just to reach the point where the first stage joins the second. Here, inside Saturn's clean white skin, are clustered the nozzles of five more engines, these fueled by liquid hydrogen and LOX. Their combined power adds a maximum second-stage thrust of 1,125,000 pounds. Another seven stories up is the hidden single nozzle of the third-stage engine, also fueled with liquid hydrogen and LOX, which will provide the climactic 225,000 pounds of thrust to break loose from the gravity of the earth.

As the elevator ascends five more stories to the top of the third stage we come to the two-ton instrument unit containing guidance and control equipment. Above this instrument ring rises the 82-foot-tall lunar package, an intricately related composite of three major flight units. First is the 34,000-pound, 19¼-foot-high Lunar Module (LM), the only unit that will actually descend to the lunar surface. Above LM looms the bullet-shaped Command and Service Module (CSM). The sharp-nosed Command Module—our cabin—rests atop the Service Module, which carries its own huge propulsion system.

Finally, above the projecting nose of the Apollo cabin, we see the Launch Escape System—the rocket and tower that would blast us free in the event of an emergency on the ground or during the first three minutes of flight.

We enter the Command Module wearing our pressure suits and "polycarbonate transparent envelopes," or helmets, which lock onto the neck ring of the suit, leaving the head free to turn inside.

Material woven from individually coated strands of fiberglass makes up the gleaming white outer layer of the suit. The coating is the same Teflon that keeps eggs from sticking to the fry pan, but for the moon voyage it serves a different purpose—guarding against abrasion.

Those of us who will go down to the moon wear 17-layered suits specially designed to shield us from the searing heat of the long lunar day and to protect our pressure garments from possible micrometeoroid damage. Such protection adds up to 54 pounds per suit, more than twice the weight of the suit the CSM pilot wears.

The atmosphere inside the cabin, under a pressure of 16 pounds per square inch, is 60 percent oxygen and 40 percent nitrogen—the latter added to reduce the risk of fire during launch-pad operations. After launch, the cabin's mixed gases will be slowly vented while oxygen pours in from storage tanks to provide an almost pure oxygen atmosphere as pressure is lowered to about 5 pounds per square inch.

As we take our places on the three Apollo couches, we can look around the 210-cubic-foot cabin that will be our home for most of the coming week. It is not exactly the palace at Versailles, but quite spacious compared with the cramped conditions of Mercury and Gemini, and air conditioning will keep the temperature at a comfortable 75° F. Although three couches all but fill the crew compartment, the center couch folds under to permit one crew member to stand and move around a bit.

The moment approaches. T-minus-3-minutes-10-seconds and counting: the Launch Director activates the automatic sequencer. T-minus-8.9-seconds: the ignition sequence begins. T-minus-6.04-seconds: the five engines of the first stage ignite and start to consume the 4,492,000 pounds of propellant, building toward a thrust that will develop roughly 180 million horsepower at maximum velocity. The skyscraper Saturn V strains at its moorings. T-minus-zero: the hold-down arms are released, but the mighty ship still is not free. A "soft release" mechanism retards the launch for half a second. Then at last, unfettered, she rises from her berth with labored dignity.

T-plus-84-seconds: maximum dynamic pressure pins us back against our couches. T-plus-2-minutes-30-seconds: the last of the lift-off fuel

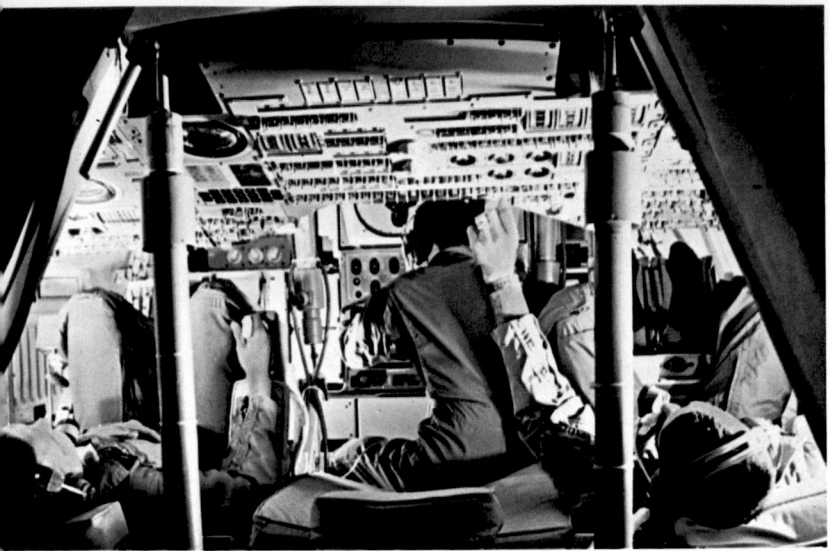

ELECTRICAL ASSEMBLERS *(below) at North American Rockwell in Downey, California, wire an Apollo mock-up. They will transfer this primary circuitry to an actual spacecraft which, at lift-off, will carry 20 miles of wire. An oven-freezer (right) simulates space conditions by simultaneously applying extreme temperatures to the Command Module: 600° F. to one side, −320° F. to the other. Astronauts Frank Borman, holding control lever, Michael Collins, sitting, and William Anders familiarize themselves with the Command Module Simulator.*

NASA (ABOVE) AND NORTH AMERICAN ROCKWELL

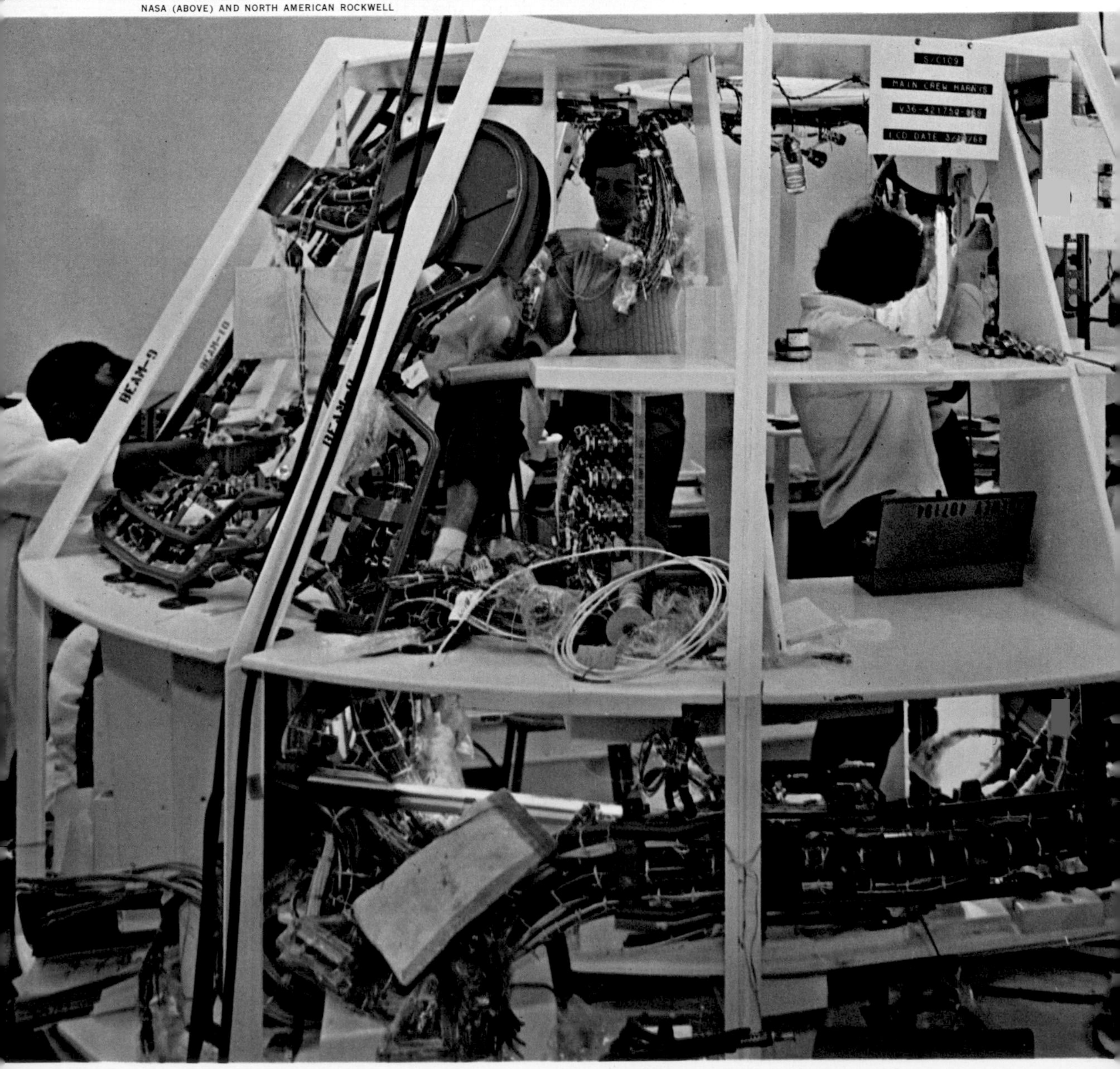

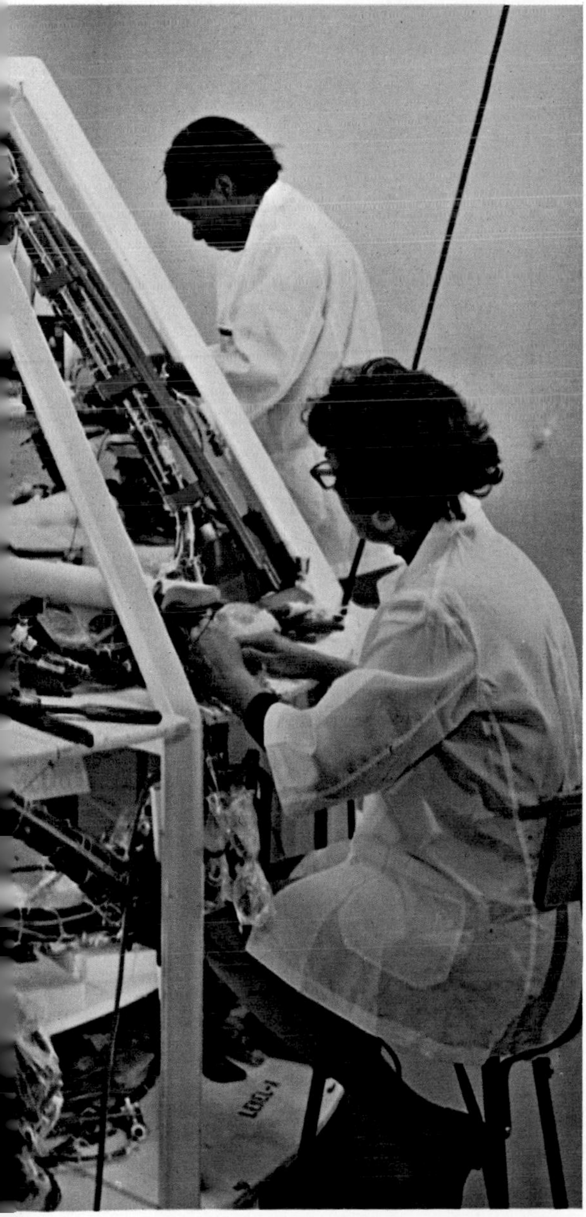

is gone, retrorockets fire to separate the first stage, and it flies off at about 200,000 feet.

The five engines of the second stage ignite for a 6-minute burn, boosting our speed to 15,300 miles an hour. Thirty seconds after ignition of the second-stage engines we feel a sharp shudder from the blast of the rocket pulling the Launch Escape System off the ship. At second-stage burn-out we are 900 nautical miles down-range, slightly above the orbital altitude of 100 nautical miles. The second stage is jettisoned.

T-plus-9-minutes: the third-stage engine ignites for its first burn of 2½ minutes, boosting velocity to the 17,500 miles per hour needed to insert us into an earth parking orbit. We are 1,500 nautical miles down-range, 100 nautical miles above the earth. The third-stage engine shuts down, and we coast in orbit.

Now we can breathe easily for a moment. We report our instrument readings to the ground, showing we have entered a safe orbit. Mission Control verifies this from its own readings and from early radar tracking by the worldwide network of stations. Then we perform our part of systems checkout and submit to remote medical examinations by the doctors at the Control Center, who monitor our respiration, pulse, heart action, blood pressure, temperature.

Our next move must be instigated from the ground. Only the Mission Director can say whether we will be permitted to proceed from earth orbit toward the moon, and if so, when. Now the final computations to determine the exact flight path begin. It's hardly a simple matter of plotting a straight line from a point on earth to the landing site on the moon, because the two points constantly change positions.

The moon revolves around the earth at 2,300 miles per hour, and the earth races around the sun at 67,000 miles per hour. Both moon and earth teeter imperceptibly back and forth as they rotate on their own axis. As we travel from one to the other the relative gravity of each changes in both direction and strength.

Our timing must be such that we arrive at the moon at a precise hour of lunar daylight that will give us just the right contrast of light and shadow to help avoid obstacles while landing; the sun must be shining on the landing site at an angle somewhere between 7° and 20°.

Such a needle's eye opens briefly during each

J-2 rocket engines, clustered at the base of a Saturn V second stage, will power Apollo for 395 seconds during man's leap to the moon. Together, the five liquid-propellant engines generate 1,125,000 pounds of thrust. Igniting 38 miles up after first-stage burnout, they will push the lunar rocket to an orbital altitude of 115 miles. The first-stage F-1 engines, providing the initial thrust for Saturn V, develop seven times the power of the J-2's. Here technicians direct positioning of J-2's at NASA's Mississippi Test Facility near Bay St. Louis. Reusable red protective coverings shield the engines during assembly and shipping.

of our earth orbits, and if all goes well we'll blast through it from our second orbit. We have chosen a "free-return" trajectory; in other words, we will be boosted out of earth orbit in such a way that our spacecraft will loop around the moon and return to earth if no additional thrust is applied.

At Mission Control Center all systems are "Go." Timed to the precise second to send our spaceship through the elusive needle's eye toward the moon, our third-stage engine re-ignites by ground command for a 5½-minute burn.

The minutes are long ones. Not until the final seconds of the burn will the spacecraft attain the velocity needed to overcome the pull of earth's gravity. For 98 percent of the time, were problems to occur, we could rely on that gravity to return the ship in an elliptical flight path for re-entry to a planned recovery area.

Finally, we get the word from Mission Control: "All systems Go! You're on your way."

As the third stage shuts down for the second and last time, we are traveling at approximately 25,000 miles an hour—slightly more than the minimum

MASSIVE SATURN V *rocket rolls out of the Kennedy Space Center's 525-foot-high Vehicle Assembly Building (right) in February, 1968, for the April 4 launching of the unmanned Apollo 6. The gigantic structure covers eight acres, providing highbay areas for four Saturn rockets. Inside, a crane lowers the third stage into place (left) as the 363-foot rocket takes shape. After assembly, Saturn V lumbers to the launch area at one mile an hour on a platform with 16 traction motors driving four double-tracked crawler units. A single lug of the track measures 7½ feet across and weighs one ton.*

YALE JOEL, LIFE © TIME, INC. (BELOW); NASA (ABOVE, LEFT); AND JOHANNA FARREN, NATIONAL GEOGRAPHIC STAFF

BILL TAUB, NASA

velocity needed to escape earth's gravity. About 15 minutes after third-stage shutdown, ground control will make the decision whether to let us continue to the moon or to order us back via the free-return route to a landing area on earth.

Again the word is "Go." If we felt like cheering, this would be a good time. But not for long; we still have much to do, beginning with a systems checkout. These tasks completed, we turn our ship toward the sun to give us the best possible illumination for docking and fire the thrusters to separate the Command and Service Module from the rest of the vehicle. Once free, we must turn completely around, dock with the Lunar Module, and jettison the now useless third stage and the Instrument Unit. This ticklish maneuver places the CSM's main engine in the clear for making corrections in our course.

Our trip will take about 70 hours. As our speed is gradually reduced by the pull of the earth upon us, then increased by the pull of the moon, our velocity will have slowed to about 3,300 miles an hour. We keep busy, taking numerous star readings as a navigational backup to ground computations, adjusting controls, reporting to Mission Control, and making mid-course corrections ordered by the Control Center.

Throughout much of the two-and-a-half day translunar coast we will be able to work in "shirt sleeves," dressed in coveralls of the same "super Beta" fabric used for the outer layer of our space suits. We follow a regular schedule, sleeping in eight-hour stretches. When it is time to rest, two of us crawl into cocoonlike sleeping bags slung beneath the right and left couches, while the third crewman beds down on the right couch within easy reach of the ship's controls.

We wake up hungry. While our "kitchen" lacks the facilities for producing a pot of fresh cocoa, we can enjoy the next best thing by adding water heated to 150° F. to a small pouch of freeze-dried

cocoa granules. At home our wives might well be preparing a quick "pick-me-up" using a similar product that they can purchase at the neighborhood supermarket.

Freeze-dried foods—which can be stored without refrigeration because all water has been removed—have made possible a more varied menu for Apollo astronauts. Again by adding hot water, we can reconstitute a surprisingly tasty dinner of roast beef, or perhaps a steaming helping of stew. Calorie content of the $1.25-a-bite menu adds up to 2,800 a day, 300 more than the Gemini fare.

Whether we attempt to enter into lunar orbit

becomes once again a decision for the Mission Director. Were he to command us to return, we would have to coast around the moon and head back toward earth. But it is far more likely at this point that we will be told to prepare to enter into a highly elliptical lunar orbit.

The crewman designated as the Lunar Module pilot already will have crawled through the tunnel to the LM to check out its systems, and we will have positioned the three-unit spacecraft so that it coasts with its main engine in front, dragging its 17-ton lunar ''bug'' behind.

As we approach the moon we begin to curve in toward it. Instruments tell us our speed is quickening and that we have entered the moon's sphere of influence. From a comparatively slow 3,600 miles an hour, we've now sped up to 4,700. It takes just 17 minutes more to boost us to 5,640 miles an hour, the point at which we fire the main engine. In 6 minutes of burn, the retrothrust reduces our velocity to 3,620 miles per hour—roughly a mile a second. Gravity and speed once again in balance, we enter lunar orbit.

Sixty nautical miles above the moon, we wait for Mission Control to confirm the accuracy of our parking orbit and advise us on our plan of descent. It is shortly after we get the "Go" for the actual lunar landing that our flight plan calls for us to sleep—if we can.

Below, mountain peaks cast jagged, lampblack shadows across strange rubbly rims and hummocks and down on ghostly foothills. Beyond, sinuous rills etch great canted plains, and rays spew out from impact craters.

Six orbits later, refreshed and back in our space suits, two of us crawl through the tunnel into the Lunar Module for another systems check. It won't be long now!

Separating LM from the Command and Service Module, we prepare to put it into its own flight path. Moving into darkness on the side of the moon away from earth, we fire the descent engine to reduce our speed and begin a sweeping elliptical orbit that will take us within 50,000 feet of the moon's surface.

But to reach that point we must coast for an hour around half the moon to the side facing earth. In free flight at the ten-mile mark, we could continue coasting and rise again in our orbit were anything to happen to discourage landing. In an emergency, we could use our engines to return to the Command and Service Module, or if they should fail, the CSM pilot could brake his ship into our orbit and pick us up.

But all continues to go well, and we fire our descent engine once more to cut our speed and begin the landing maneuver. In 450 fast-moving

seconds, covering 243 nautical miles, we have trimmed our velocity from 5,500 feet per second to 600 and our altitude from 50,000 feet to 9,000.

We fire our thrusters to tilt the LM nearly vertical, giving us our first good look at the landing area—still eight nautical miles ahead and 8,600 feet below. Our faces are glued to the twin triangular windows of the Lunar Module.

"Can you see the landing area?" a voice in our earphones asks.

"Yes, we see it bright and clear. It looks good."

But there is little time for talk. The final approach provides barely a hundred seconds to survey the landing area as we descend to 500 feet, cutting back our velocity to 50 feet per second.

"It still looks good. We're going down."

How hard the landing will be depends on the pilot's split-second timing. He watches for the light to signal that the thin, wire-like probes extending below the dish-shaped landing pads have touched the surface.

Speed: 4 feet per second.

Light on! Engine off!

Touch down!

We made it! We're on the moon!

From Mission Control in Houston a cheer goes up that is heard round the world—as well as on the moon. "Beautiful! Beautiful!" shouts the pilot of the Command and Service Module.

Safely down, we are still four hours from putting a foot on the moon's surface. First we must check the condition of the cabin and report to Mission Control and to our friend orbiting above, and go through a simulated lunar launch countdown. This done, we begin to outfit ourselves for our lunar excursion, helping the pilot strap on the Portable Life Support System containing oxygen, radio, batteries, and other no-less-important gear.

RICHARD PIPES (BELOW) AND RALPH MORSE, LIFE, NASA

SEARING MASSES *of steam and flame erupt from Saturn V at lift-off from Kennedy Space Center. The mighty rocket launched Apollo 6 into earth orbit to test the unmanned spacecraft and its heat shield during re-entry. A camera with wide-angle lens, mounted on the umbilical tower 360 feet up, and operated remotely, shows a 20-ton swing arm moving back to release the rocket. At left, Astronaut Lovell briefs author William R. Shelton on the Apollo lunar mission at the Manned Spacecraft Center in Houston, Texas. Lovell holds the world's space distance record—7,300,000 miles in 428.2 hours.*

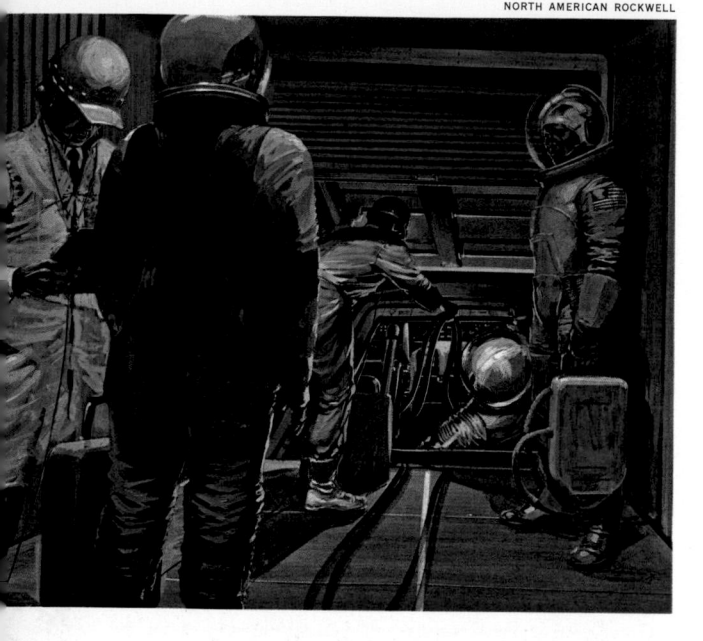

MOON-BOUND ASTRONAUTS *board their Apollo spacecraft after a final checkout in the service tower at Cape Kennedy's Launch Complex 39. In an artist's conception of the lunar flight, planned for 1969, Saturn V's second-stage engines ignite (top) following first stage burn-out, 150 seconds after lift-off. The second stage powers Apollo to a speed of 15,300 miles an hour, then falls away as the third stage takes over (middle), pushing the spacecraft into earth orbit. After circling the planet in a parking orbit for two or three revolutions, the third-stage engine fires once more, hurling the payload on its course toward the moon.*

Each 20-moon-pound backpack contains a four-hour supply of oxygen, plus a small emergency canister good for 30 minutes.

Finally, we don gloves and visors, and carefully check the pressure of our bulky space suits. Now we can depressurize the cabin and open the forward hatch.

We ease out of the opening behind the pilot and onto the platform outside. We climb slowly and carefully down the ladder to the moon's surface 15 feet below. After gathering at least three pounds of random soil samples in a bag, we pass them up to the Commander for storage inside the spacecraft. This is to insure that we will take this much of the moon back with us, should we be required to make a hurried departure.

Gradually familiarizing ourselves with the eerie sensation of gravity only one-sixth that of earth, we check the condition of the LM and report to the envious Commander, who will remain inside the craft.

"It's like walking on old snow," the world learns as we crunch slowly along, marking our lunar trail with inch-deep bootprints sunk into the basaltic surface.

But snow it is not. Temperatures of the two-week-long lunar day may reach the 250° F. mark. However, our air-conditioned space suits and the water-cooled garments we wear close to our skin keep us comfortable. An intricate network of tubes carries chilled water from the backpack all

around the body, then back for recooling and re-circulation. But the pressurized suits are unwieldly for some tasks and our huge protective gloves, although surprisingly flexible, were not designed for threading needles.

Next comes the job of preparing a second and more sophisticated collection of lunar soil and rocks—about 35 earth-pounds in all. These samples will give scientists waiting on earth their first "close-up" look at the moon's surface. Acting as their eyes for the moment, we carefully document each item.

Encumbered by our many-layered space suits, we now fully realize that performing even simple moon-tasks makes slow, arduous work. In two hours, we have ventured only a few steps toward the lunar horizon, roughly a mile away.

Each way we turn, the view becomes more awesome than the one before—until we look in the direction of the low-level sun where a flood of light fills the shadows and takes away the texture of the lunar surface. No widespread erosion, in the conventional sense, has marred the surface. It is as if we were looking at the true face of history —the record, the calendar, the manuscript of much of the solar system's past, its present, and, perhaps, its future.

It would be impossible to sketch the outlines of the hundreds of craters within our line of sight. Some are the size of a 50-cent piece, others no larger than birdbaths. These we must document on color film with our cameras.

Jogged by the LM Commander that it is time once more to climb aboard our spacecraft, we turn, almost reluctantly, toward the waiting Lunar Module and our last brief moon-hours.

To some it may seem ironic that we have trav-

1   2

Intricate in-flight maneuvers put man on the moon: Half an hour after Apollo leaves earth orbit on a lunar heading, its four adapter panels open (1), disclosing the Lunar Module—the vehicle that will actually touch down on the moon; the Command and Service Module begins pulling away for an on-course docking operation. After moving about 100 feet out, it performs a turn-around (2), docks gently with the Lunar Module (3) and extracts the buglike craft (4). The moonship then coasts on toward its target. After a three-day voyage at an average speed of more than 3,000 mph, the craft enters moon orbit, where the Lunar Module, manned by two astronauts, separates and begins its descent (5). A powerful rocket gently brakes it to the selected landing area (6). Finally, the first American steps onto the pitted lunar surface—and into history (7). The Command and Service Module, carrying the third crew member, orbits overhead. The two astronauts probably will remain on the moon for about 24 hours— one will stay on board the craft as a back-up man, while the other works outside. This lunar pioneer will collect samples of rock and dust, photograph the terrain, and explore the area surrounding the Lunar Module. On a later excursion to the moon, astronauts may emplace the Apollo Lunar Surface Experiments Package, an assortment of scientific instruments that will be left behind to record such matters as heat flow, seismic activity, and the make-up of the lunar atmosphere.

RYAN AERONAUTICAL CO. (BELOW, RIGHT), NASA (OPPOSITE, LOWER), AND NORTH AMERICAN ROCKWELL

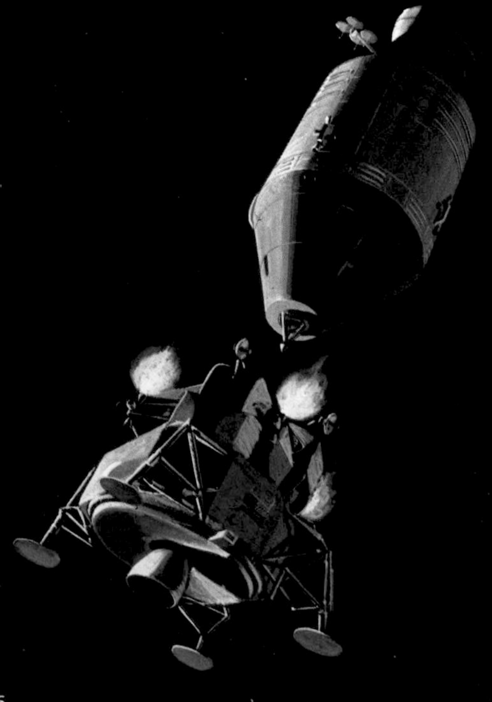

3

4

UNITED STATES

7

eled so far, at such great expense, barely to have scratched the moon's surface. But we have left our footprints, and in them others soon will follow. Our experience will make it possible for fellow space adventurers to make more detailed explorations, and they will bring with them tools to study not only the moon's surface but also its atmosphere and its interior.

The Apollo Lunar Surface Experiments Package being developed for the lunar-landing program contains many such tools — instruments to study the charged particles of the solar wind, the magnetic characteristics of the moon, and cosmic rays and micrometeoroids. Other devices will measure the moon's seismic activity and compare the radioactivity deep beneath the lunar surface with that of the earth's mantle. Powered by an atomic generator, these instruments will continue to send lunar "weather" reports long after the men who set them up have returned to earth.

After eating and resting, we begin our prelaunch checkout with Mission Control and the CSM pilot. The time has come to return to earth.

LM's descent stage, with its strong, spindly legs that helped us touch down softly, now serves as a launch platform. It will stay behind on the moon. We ignite the ascent engine, rise into a computer-calculated elliptical orbit, then change our course to intercept the CSM.

Sighting the mother ship about 30 miles away, we begin the rendezvous maneuver, using our reaction-control thrusters to regulate our approach speed. The pilot of the Command and Service Module may also maneuver toward us, since either vehicle can assume the active role in docking. Docking completed, we crawl back into the CSM and a joyful reunion with the third member of our crew. How spacious the cabin seems after the cramped quarters of the LM.

Now it is time to leave the lunar parking orbit and begin the long flight back to earth. We jetti-

ELONGATED SHADOWS *streak a simulated lunar landscape at the Manned Spacecraft Center. Astronaut Don Lind, wearing a pressure suit, tests the Seismic Experiment Subsystem that will investigate the nature and source of the moon's seismic activity. Another component of the Apollo Lunar Surface Experiments Package rests on the surface. The Apollo expedition will touch down on the moon at the beginning of the 14-day period of sunlight.*

son the Lunar Module, which will remain in orbit around the moon — mute testimony to our brief visit.

While behind the moon we fire the main engine of the Service Module, starting our craft on the return flight. For two and a half days we coast homeward, making navigational studies, preparing reports, and remaining in continuous contact with ground control.

As we come under the influence of earth's gravity, our speed increases to about 25,000 miles an hour. Minutes before slamming into the atmosphere like a meteor, we jettison the Service Module. Now all that remains of a once incredibly complex rocket and spacecraft train is the top-shaped Command Module.

A ided by Mission Control's massive banks of computers, we aim toward a narrow corridor in the earth's atmosphere a scant 40 miles deep and 300 miles wide. Everything depends on our descent angle; it must be just right. If it is too steep, we'll enter too sharply and deceleration forces will be greater than we can endure. If the angle is too shallow, our spacecraft will skip into a new and unwanted orbit. Were this to happen, we could run out of oxygen before our new orbit decayed and let us descend to earth — unlike the Mercury or Gemini craft, Apollo does not have retrorockets to reduce its velocity for re-entry.

We maneuver the spacecraft by firing our jet thrusters and rolling it to change the direction of its lift. To some degree it is like steering a glider as we thread our way between the unseen guard rails of our "off ramp" to earth.

As the spacecraft plummets through the thickening atmosphere, it forms a shock wave of compressed molecules ahead of its large blunt heat shield, pushing the rest of the onrushing air away. Even with such designed-in protection, our heat shield still has to endure temperatures as high as 5,000° F., but the interior of the cabin remains a comfortable 75°.

The fiery re-entry over, we plummet to within 25,000 feet of earth, where we jettison the parachute housing cover and deploy the drogue chutes. At 12,000 feet the pilot chutes spin out, followed by the main chutes. The latter, fully open in eight seconds, slow the spacecraft to a landing speed of 25 feet a second. Below us, we know, waits a recovery fleet of ships and helicopters.

Splash-down! We're home!

After splash-down, recovery procedures become quite different from those of an earth orbital mission. Before climbing out of our spacecraft, we must dress in special coveralls that will keep us isolated from the earth's environment. NASA technicians gingerly transport us in quarantine to the Lunar Receiving Laboratory at the Manned Spacecraft Center at Houston. The doctors will let us out only after they are quite sure we haven't picked up some virulent contaminant on the moon that could threaten life and health on earth.

In the time-honored tradition that began in the 2d century A.D. with Lucian's tale of ascending to the moon in a wind-powered ship, this account — written before a manned Apollo flight — contains a modicum of fiction. It also contains a rather large portion of optimism, for it has assumed an unlikely sequence of successes and has not dared to guess at any of the specific hazards and dangers that in the past have become serious threats to mission and life on flights of far less complexity.

Project Apollo is no armchair adventure. Its successful completion requires no less than the best technological talent of the entire Nation, a budget in the billions, and the dedication and energies of the hundreds of thousands of people who helped produce the incredible Saturn V rocket and the even more incredible spacecraft itself. This great, intricate, enfabled chariot, because of the people who have fashioned her, has earned the right to attempt a response to the words of President John F. Kennedy in his 1962 State of the Union Message:

"And our objective in making this effort, which we hope will place one of our citizens on the moon, is to develop in a new frontier of science, commerce and cooperation, the position of the United States and the free world. This nation belongs among the first to explore it. And among the first, if not the first, we shall be."

ASCENT ENGINE FIRING, *the Lunar Module lifts off from the moon, using its expended descent stage as a launch platform (1). After reaching moon orbit, the Lunar Module intercepts the Command and Service Module and docks (2); the lunar explorers then transfer to the command craft. The reunited crew, ready to return to earth, jettisons the lunar landing vehicle (3), leaving it to wheel about the moon. A two-minute blast of the Service Module's engines (4) catapults the astronauts earthward.*

8 / THE PROMISE OF SPACE: WHERE WILL IT LEAD?

"This is as close as I can get to actually going to the moon," said my host, physicist Persa Raymond Bell, as we stepped from an elevator 60 feet underground. We had come to look at the room where Dr. Bell and his colleagues will conduct radioactivity tests on the first rock and soil samples brought back from the moon.

Above us rose a three-story, 8.5-million-dollar building that exists entirely for the future—the Lunar Receiving Laboratory at Houston's Manned Spacecraft Center. My guide was Chief of the Center's Lunar and Earth Sciences Division, and manager of the unique laboratory.

"This labyrinthine entrance," Dr. Bell said as we walked down a silver-painted tunnel toward a 90 degree turn, "is designed to keep out cosmic rays, which can travel only in straight lines." At the end of the tunnel we emerged into a spotless silver and white room. In one corner stood the gamma ray counter; it looked somewhat like a squat, stolid furnace.

"The counter exists for only one purpose—to tell us how much and what kinds of radioactivity lunar rocks have," Dr. Bell explained. "With this information, we can learn a great deal about the moon, including the number of years the samples lay exposed at the surface."

The depth of the room—along with eight-foot-thick walls of concrete and natural stone—eliminates four-fifths of the bombarding rays; a lithium-lead mantle around the counter blocks the rest. "That way, we can be sure our count includes only emissions from the moon samples," Dr. Bell said.

As we rode up in the elevator, he talked enthusiastically about the future: "Our work really begins when the astronauts return with the first lunar samples. Think what this means! We've never really had a preserved fragment from space. We've only had meteorites seared by intense heat as they plunged through our atmosphere. But the rocks brought back by the astronauts will be packed in a vacuum much like that found on the moon."

For the next three hours, Dr. Bell and I toured

LUNAR COLONY *of the 21st century houses research scientists and visitors from earth, almost a quarter of a million miles away. Spherical craft shuttle passengers to an orbiting space station. In this artist's conception, astronautical engineers survey the moon's pocked surface with the tools of tomorrow.*

the elaborate facilities designed to protect the lunar samples from the earth environment, and the earth against any possibility of contamination from the moon. The inner laboratory exists in nearly perfect isolation; even the garbage will be decontaminated. Everything that moves across the barrier must go in and out of ultraviolet or high-temperature sterilization chambers.

A mobile home will transport the returned astronauts to the Center where they will complete a three-week quarantine. Their families will see them only through glass. So strict will be the quarantine, in fact, that an operating room has been provided for any surgical emergency.

The 40 to 50 pounds of precious lunar material will be even more rigorously isolated in a huge vacuum chamber. Some 120 biologists, chemists, electron microscopy experts, and other specialists will sterilize, weigh, cut, grind, analyze, and sort the rocks, using remote-controlled equipment. Other samples will go to more than a hundred laboratories across the world at the end of the

quarantine period. Some of the material will be ground into solutions and injected into white mice to see if there is any adverse effect.

"We don't really expect to find dangerous organisms in the lunar samples," Dr. Bell explained, "but you must remember that this port of entry has responsibility for our entire planet. We can't be too careful."

At the conclusion of my visit, I asked Dr. Bell, "When the first moon rocks come in, where will you be?"

"Right here, waiting," he said, smiling broadly.

As I left the Lunar Receiving Laboratory, I walked across the "campus" of the Manned Spacecraft Center. In a complex of 40 buildings, some of them filled with computers, other key work affecting man's future in space goes on. Men and women plot tomorrow's adventures, grappling with the problems of space stations, planetary exploration, satellites, and man himself.

Similar work is going on at NASA's nine other centers, at California's Jet Propulsion Laboratory, at the U. S. Air Force Manned Orbital Laboratory at Edwards Air Force Base, California, as well as

SPENT SECOND STAGE of a Saturn I-B houses an orbiting laboratory with winglike solar panels. The cutaway shows the rocket partitioned by aluminum grids like those in the simulation at right. Experiments in weightless living will range over man's daily activities, even including the best method of taking a shower. The subject below uses a dishwasher spray during brief weightlessness induced aboard a U. S. Air Force plane in parabolic flight.

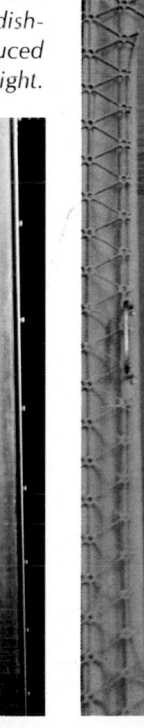

TRACKING THE STARS *with a clarity never known before, a manned astronomical observatory of tomorrow peers at the heavens from above the obscuring haze of the atmosphere. Earth's shimmering veil of gases and water vapor blurs telescopic images of planets and stars. "Once we get into space," astronomers say, "we can expect to see distant objects invisible to us now because their light doesn't penetrate the atmosphere." At left, an astronaut checks the power system and control console of the Saturn I Workshop in mock-up. Dressed in a suit designed for interior work during construction of the space station, the crewman stands in "Dutch shoes." These slippers, firmly attached to the grid floor with removable metal pins, anchor the weightless astronaut.*

at dozens of university and industrial laboratories.

The nation that had recovered from the fiery Vanguard explosion to mount an energetic, sustained, and often inspired thrust across a new and hazardous frontier, was still on the eve of incredible journeys. In the first ten years, man had charged into space as if his very existence depended upon reaching it. And now he has erected a durable bridge into the cosmos.

But where does it lead? And why are we going?

As a benefit to science, man crosses the bridge to discover the nature of the universe, to study the physics of the atmosphere, to comprehend the origin and evolution of the solar system — all goals that may involve risk and high drama.

To Soviet author Igor M. Zabelin, man's thrust into space represents his instinctive preparation for the settlement of other planets as he overpopulates and pollutes his own.

Some economists believe the cost of space exploration can become a substitute for war as an economic and technological stimulant. In the final analysis, however, perhaps it is man's natural inquisitiveness that drives him toward the stars.

Whatever the reason, man's penetration of space appears permanent and irrevocable. John F. Kennedy once used a story by the Irish writer Frank O'Connor to illustrate the nature of our foothold in space.

"As a boy," Kennedy pointed out, "he and his friends would make their way across the countryside, and when they came to an orchard wall that seemed too high and too doubtful to try and too difficult to permit their voyage to continue, they took off their hats and tossed them over the wall and then they had no choice but to follow them."

The space probes sent from earth are, in a sense, the tossed caps and *shlyapy* that it is now man's destiny to follow — whether he be New Englander or Siberian. But what of the future, beyond the initial landing on the moon?

In the first place, simply landing once on the moon will solve few of the enigmas surrounding our nearest neighbor in space. Astrogeologist Shoemaker estimates that many flights and geologic surveys must be made before we can answer even the question of whether the moon was once a part of earth or whether it was captured from

space by earth's gravity, or whether the moon and the earth were formed at the same time in the same fashion as uniform parts of the solar system.

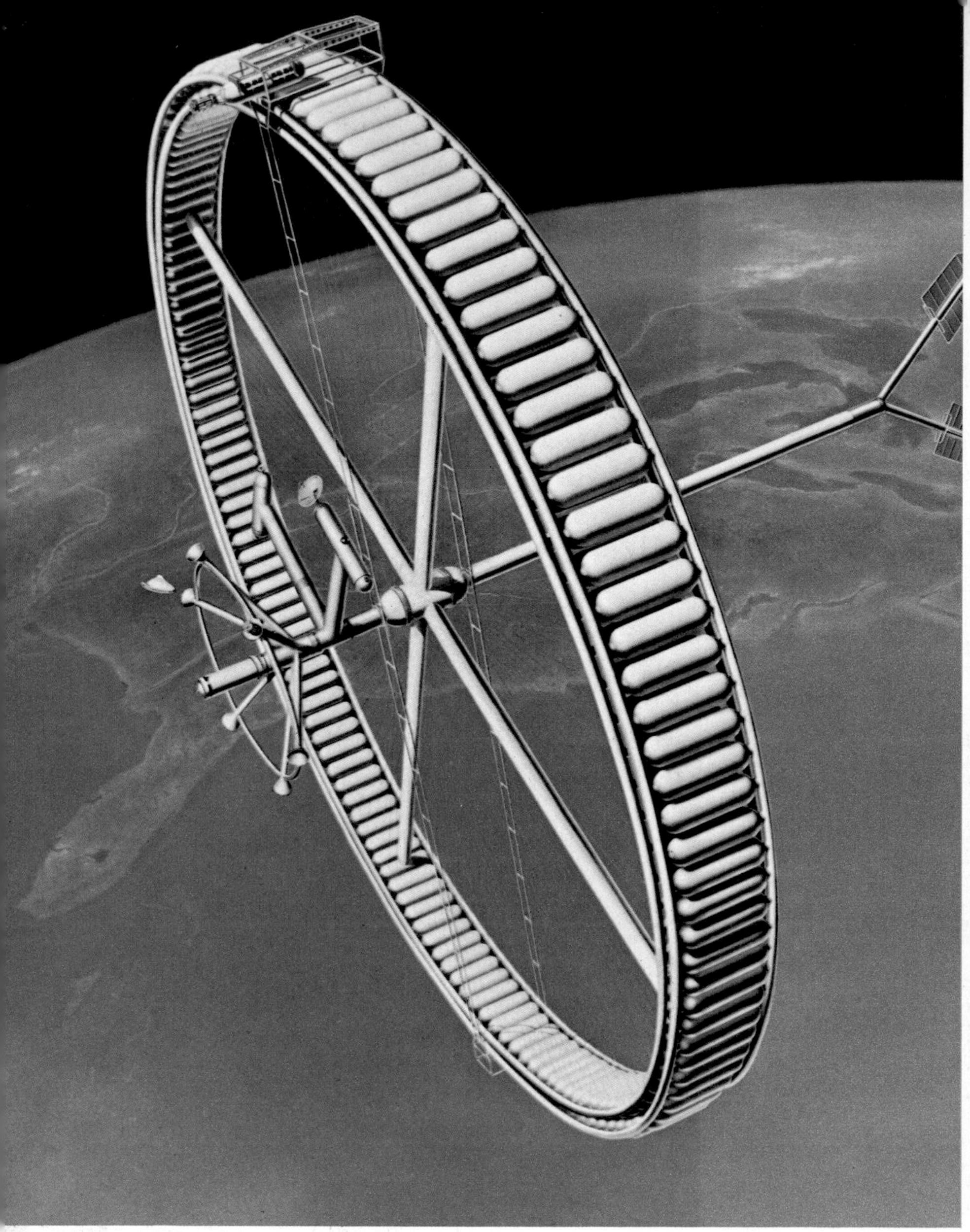

"Many people have the idea," Shoemaker told me, "that once we land an astronaut on the moon and return him to earth with his rock samples, we can suddenly come to firm conclusions about the moon's origin and history. This is simply not so. For one thing, determining the moon's origin may require us to search out the oldest rocks on the moon, and this will take time."

In addition to follow-up flights to the moon, NASA hopes to modify Apollo equipment for earth orbital missions. A striking example is the Saturn I Workshop, actually a large, converted hydrogen

CELESTIAL CITY of the future wheels silently to create its own artificial gravity 200 miles above Florida. A tiny triangular space liner (left), approaches one of the funnel-shaped docking collars. The cutaway at right reveals a hospital, a computerized library, a dining room, and shuttle tubes. Other sections will hold swimming pools, ice rinks—even a zero-g chamber where the visitor can experience the exhilaration of weightlessness.

fuel tank that scientists expect to put into service during the 1970's.

After lift-off by the first stage of a powerful Saturn I-B rocket, the second stage—the S-IV-B—will boost itself into orbit 260 miles high. Three astronauts will ride another Saturn I-B to intercept the

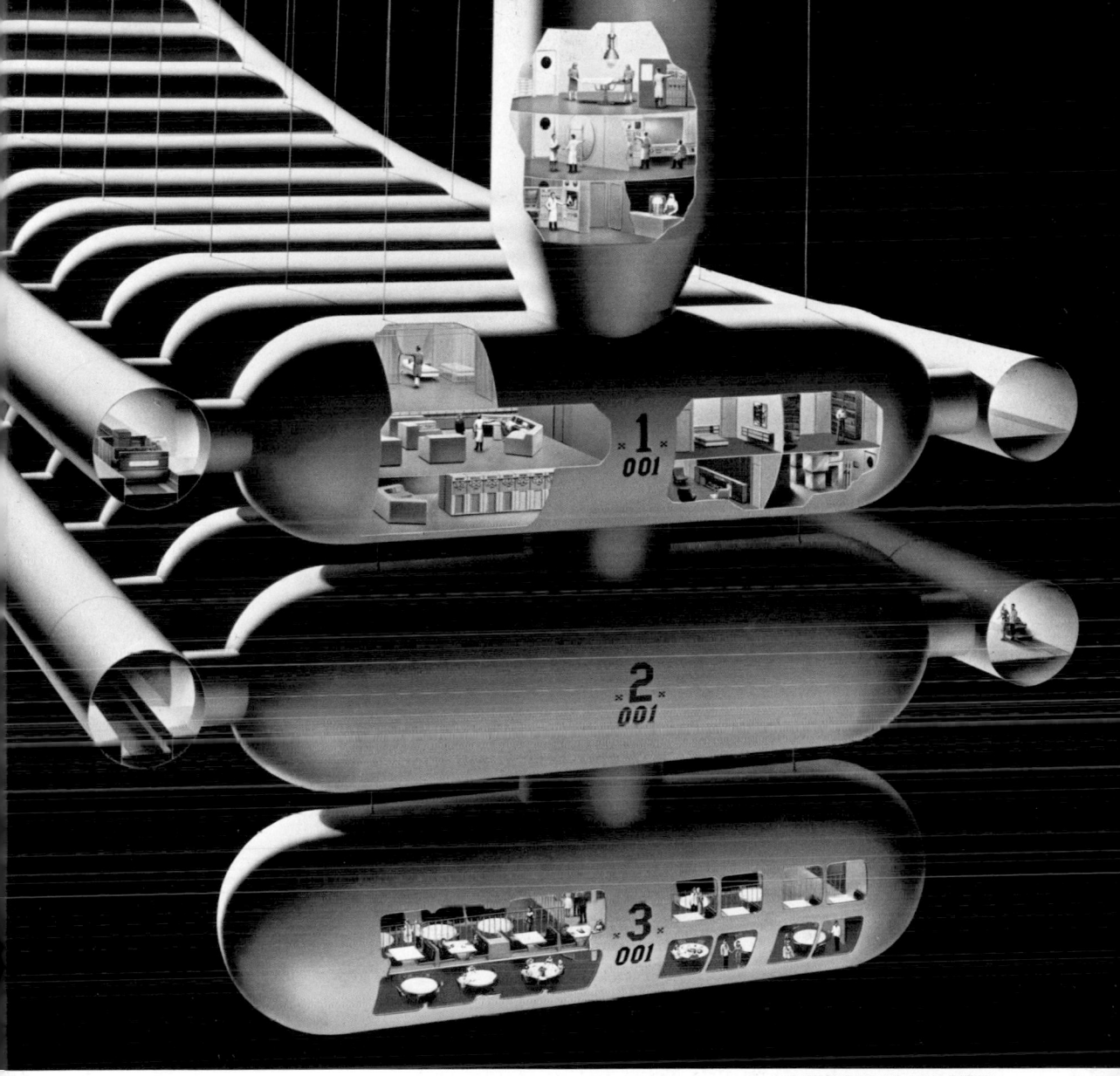

empty tank, dock with it, and make sure the last of the hydrogen is vented, then pressurize the workshop with oxygen and nitrogen.

Entering the tank through an air lock, they will pull out partitions, bunks, tables, and seats—all attached to the walls when the tank was built. They will plug in pre-installed electrical systems, and stow food and supplies for 28 days. The prefabricated space station, 22 feet in diameter and 35 feet deep, will provide the three astronauts with 10,000 cubic feet of room on two floors.

The first of the three missions planned for the workshop would last about a month. According to Dr. George E. Mueller, NASA's Associate Administrator for Manned Space Flight, "We are limited to something like four weeks on this flight because of the need to build up our understanding of the effects of weightlessness over a period of time on the crew. . . ." At mission's end the astronauts will leave the vehicle in orbit and return to earth.

The second mission, planned to last for 28 to 56 days, calls for astronauts to conduct more extensive medical investigations, as well as experiments in communication, meteorology, astrophysics, and in determining the location of natural resources both in the oceans and on land.

On a third trip, NASA plans to launch a solar observatory for making manned observations of the sun without the distorting effects of the lower atmosphere. The practical applications, according

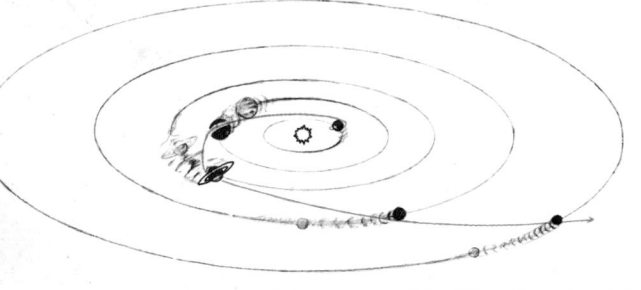

"GRAND TOUR" in space would utilize the planets' gravitational fields to boost an unmanned fly-by probe past Jupiter, Saturn, Uranus, and Neptune. Ideal alignment of the planets for the 8.9-year trip will occur in 1978, but not again until 2158.

MECHANICAL SPACE SCOUTS in the 1970's will precede man in his exploration of the solar system. Below, a quarter-scale model of a scientific package designed to land on Mars flexes its instruments in California's White Mountains. Legs of the Automated Biological Laboratory unfold to hold it upright. A picture-taking periscope transmits surface images. A remote sampler, the tiny cable-car device dangling from the stay wire, travels to the surface, collects material, and returns. Gas chromatographs examine the sample for molecular content, and another device attempts to grow cultures of any micro-organisms captured. Thirty-five separate experiments can test the environment for signs of life. At right, a soft-lander probe fires its retrorocket as it approaches the ringed planet Saturn.

PHILCO-FORD CORPORATION

to Dr. Mueller, are a better understanding of radio blackouts and magnetic storms, and of the sun itself.

Solar cells, by converting sunlight into electricity, will power the motors needed to position the telescope. This method of acquiring and using energy particularly intrigues Dr. Mueller. "Approximately 32,000 times as much energy as the human race is currently using reaches the earth's surface each year from the sun," he points out. "Were we able to harness efficiently a sizable portion of this energy, our energy source problem could be solved."

Small space stations may soon lead to permanent, more versatile and sophisticated orbiting laboratories. Dr. Robert R. Gilruth, Director of the Manned Spacecraft Center, foresees a rotating space station with room for up to 100 men that might be assembled by the late 1970's. About 600 feet long and weighing a million pounds, the station would be launched in three major sections by a trio of Saturn V rockets. After assembly in space, it would spin about its hub three and a half times a minute, inducing a gravitational force almost equal to earth's.

Businessmen look with keen interest toward space. Some believe that substantial savings may become possible through manufacturing such things as miniaturized electronic circuitry and computers in orbiting factories that utilize the natural cleanliness and vacuum of space.

Doctors look to the day when patients with heart ailments will live longer, thanks to treatment in the gravity-free wards of space hospitals. Physiologist Eugene B. Konecci, who teaches at the University of Texas, believes that orbital hospitals will be a boon to severe-burn patients. A germ-free environment and zero-g will offer them comfort unavailable on earth.

"I can envision executives and other people leaving their terrestrial jobs for their annual physicals and rest in space," Konecci says. "Preventive maintenance would be performed on them in the orbital health maintenance station . . . while they go through a battery of tests and undergo corrective surgery or other treatment."

But before orbiting hospitals can become a practical reality, the role of women in space must surely be dramatically enlarged. Thus far, only Russia has orbited a woman, Valentina Tereshkova. Mercury astronauts, chosen from the ranks

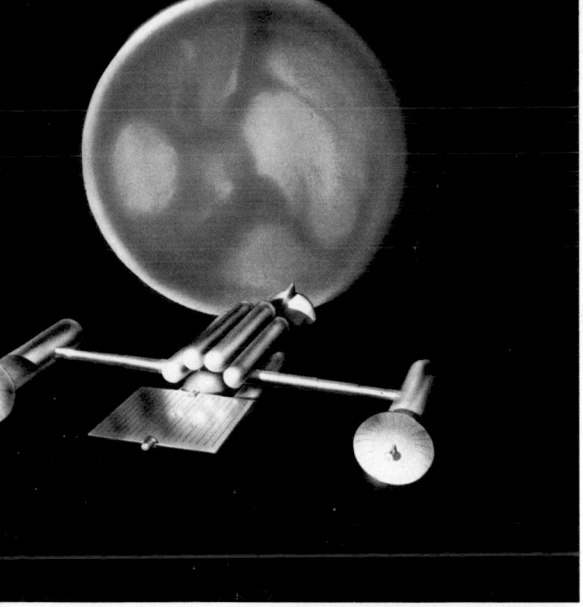

FROM EARTH TO MARS: *Nuclear-power spaceship, a possibility for the 1980's, pushes away from earth (far left), ringed with fuel packs. With nuclear power plant and outrigger modules deployed (near left), it hurtles toward the red planet, its winglike earth-return module riding at the nose. After landing on the stark Martian desert, astronauts install an antenna and a portable meteorological station on a hillside. Scientists say the first explorers on Mars will find the most earthlike planet in our solar system, with clouds, winds, and winter frosts.*

of military test pilots with more than 1,000 hours of jet-flight time, naturally included no women. But all that is changing. NASA officials expect women astronauts to take scientific roles within ten years.

Even as man gains experience in orbital flight, the role of unmanned satellites is growing. Scientists have already developed startling sensing devices, ranging from cameras with infrared film that reveal the presence of underground water to instruments so sensitive they can measure ice thickness in the oceans. In the future, lasers reflected from the moon may unlock secrets of the moon's interior through the detection of variations in gravitational force.

Nor will the other planets be exempt from man's probing. The Russians have said they will still make interplanetary flights. U. S. scientists continue to work toward explorations reaching to the edge of deep space.

Studies of Venus, Jupiter, and Mars show that the red planet is more earthlike, and it has been given scientific priority. Mars has both a livable temperature and a gravitational field strong enough to retain an atmosphere, largely of carbon dioxide. Seasonal and color changes visible on its surface may be simply dust hills shifting with the winds, or may indicate plant life.

With two Mars fly-bys, scheduled for 1969, the United States plans to photograph 20 percent of the planet's surface, and in 1971 two attempts will be made to put instruments into a Martian orbit. Later in the decade, if all goes well, a satellite orbiting Mars will drop an instrument package to collect data during its descent through the atmosphere, and on the surface. Once safely down, the lander will test soil samples, register temperature changes, and analyze material just below the planet's surface.

FICTION FORECASTS FACT: *Buck Rogers comic strip uses the term "astronaut" in this panel drawn in 1936. The adventure series heralded the Space Age with rocket belts, interplanetary travel, and space stations. At right, in an artist's conception, engineers on a gravity-free platform assemble a craft designed to explore the solar system. Robot arms of a tug guide a fuel tank toward the spaceship. Rockets assembled and launched at such stations would require less propulsion than those launched from earth where gravity pulls more strongly.*

Space scientists propose a fuel-saving maneuver to aid in exploring other planets. With about the same amount of fuel required for a trip to Venus, a deep-space probe using the Venusian gravity as a sort of sling-shot would attempt to reach the vicinity of Mercury, the planet nearest the sun.

The interplanetary space between Venus and Mars has already been probed successfully by Pioneer and Mariner spacecraft. During the next ten years, they will fly past Mars, through the asteroid belt, and then on to the vicinity of Jupiter. On the way, the probes will study the asteroids, helping us to determine whether the larger ones should be converted into observatories, as some engineers suggest, or whether it is feasible to use them as platforms for launching spacecraft beyond the solar system.

No specific plans exist for U. S. manned flights

to the planets, and some scientists oppose such missions on the grounds that man is superfluous in space, that automated vehicles can do the job.

Others, including Dr. Ernst Stuhlinger of the Marshall Space Flight Center at Huntsville, Alabama, are convinced that man should build nuclear-power spaceships to visit his neighboring planets in person, and that it is time to begin.

"We could make the round trip to Mars in about 14 months," Stuhlinger told me, "but I would not recommend that man ever attempt to go into deep space in a single vehicle. For the exploration of Mars, we should send a small armada of spaceships. If something happened to one of them, the crew of about eight men could transfer to another one and keep going."

Still other scientists believe the search for life should bypass the solar system and concentrate far out among the stars themselves. But even if we could find a way to travel at the speed of light— 186,000 miles a second—it would still take us four and a half years to reach our nearest neighbor star, Alpha Centauri.

So our exploring may be done from orbital or lunar observatories, with scientists watching and listening across the void for signs of life.

Or perhaps, with the incredible advances in technology, we'll discover a way to communicate with other star systems, if intelligent beings exist there. Maybe then our compulsion to make the trip will vanish.

But I don't think so.

"Whenever man has had the means of exploration and discovery," John Glenn once told me, "history shows that he has had the courage to make the journey—no matter where it might take him."

I think Glenn is right, that man will heed his inner urgings, that he will cross the bridge into the cosmos simply because—like the beckoning mountain—it is there.

EXTRATERRESTRIAL PIONEERS *explore a new-found frontier on Mars. Lifted by gas jets, cameramen make film studies of the dusty terrain. Other crewmen, living in inflated igloos, will chart the surface. A dish antenna beams data to earth, and a landing taxi blasts toward orbit, where a parent ship waits to take the 21st-century explorers home. Of man's future in space, the author says, "not until life moved out to dry land could it see the stars, and life will not be content until it has reached them."*

PAINTING BY ROBERT McCALL FROM LIFE MAGAZINE

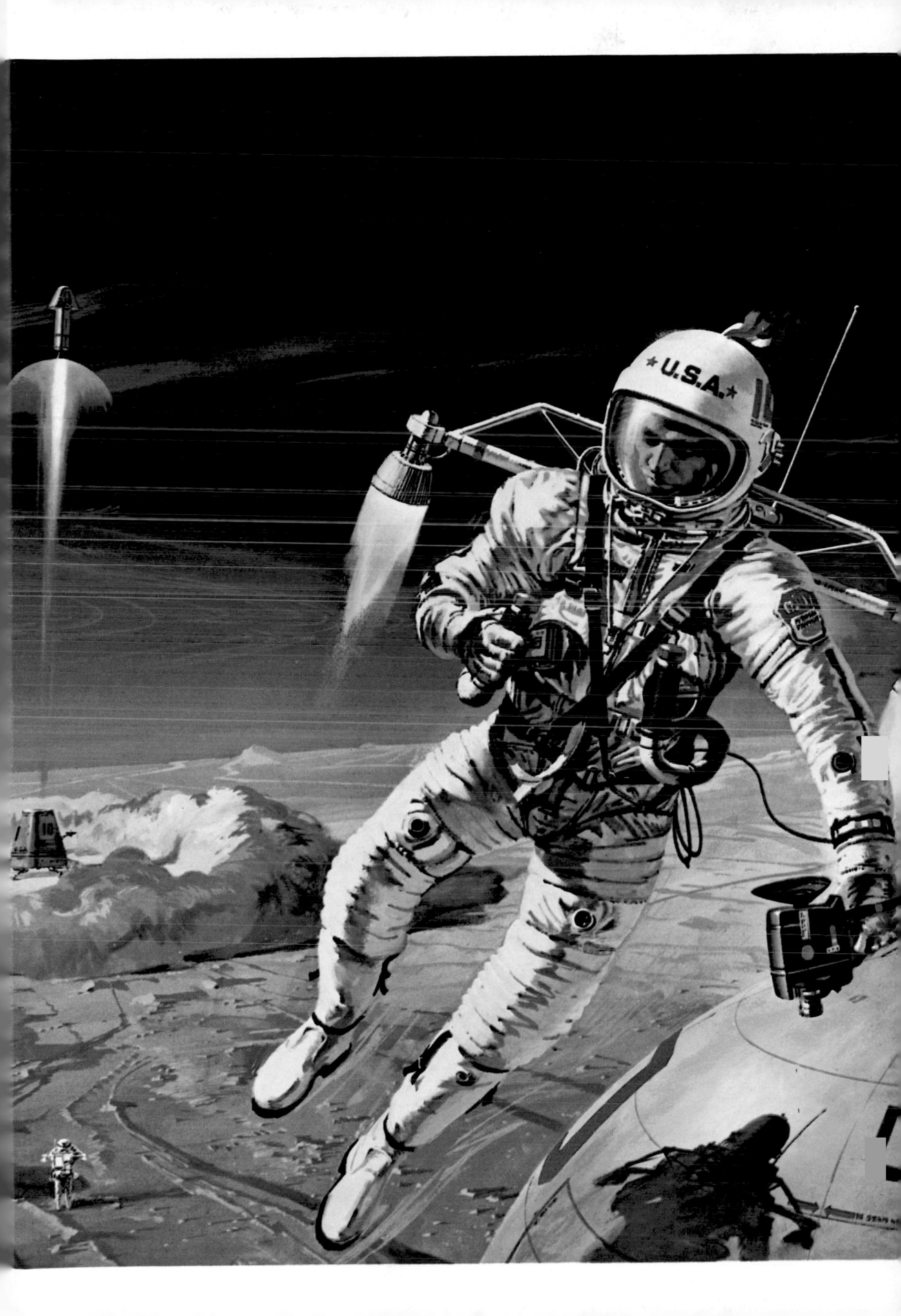

INDEX
Illustrations references appear in *italics*.

ADDITIONAL REFERENCES

For additional reading, you may wish to refer to these NATIONAL GEOGRAPHIC articles and to check the Cumulative Index for related material.

"Footprints on the Moon," by Hugh L. Dryden, March, 1964. "Telephone a Star," by Rowe Findley, May, 1962. "Cape Canaveral's 6,000-mile Shooting Gallery," Oct., 1959; "Exploring Tomorrow With the Space Agency," July, 1960; "Reaching for the Moon," Feb., 1959, all by Allan C. Fisher, Jr. "The Sun," by Herbert Friedman, Nov., 1965. "The Making of an Astronaut," by Robert R. Gilruth, Jan., 1965. "Space Satellites, Tools of Earth Research," by Heinz Haber, April, 1956. "The Flight of Freedom 7," by Carmault B. Jackson, Jr., M.D., Sept., 1961. "How Man-Made Satellites Can Affect Our Lives," by Joseph Kaplan, Dec., 1957. "The Long, Lonely Leap," by Capt. Joseph W. Kittinger, Jr., USAF, Dec., 1960. "The Solar Eclipse From a Jet," by Wolfgang B. Klemperer, Nov., 1963. "U. S. Air Force: Power for Peace," by Gen. Curtis E. LeMay, Sept., 1965. "The Earth From Orbit," by Paul D. Lowman, Jr., Nov., 1966.

"Four-Ocean Navy in the Nuclear Age," by Thomas W. McKnew, Feb., 1965. "The Laser's Bright Magic," by Thomas Meloy, Dec., 1966. "Exploring Our Neighbor World, the Moon," by Donald H. Menzel, Feb., 1958. "First Color Portraits of the Heavens," by William C. Miller, May, 1959. "Surveyor: Candid Camera on the Moon," by Homer E. Newell, Oct., 1966. "We Saw the World From the Edge of Space," by Comdr. Malcolm D. Ross, USNR, Nov., 1961. "Mars, a New World to Explore," by Carl Sagan, Dec., 1967. "Mariner Scans a Lifeless Venus," May, 1963; "Robots to the Moon," Oct., 1962, both by Frank Sartwell. "The Pilot's Story: Astronaut Shepard's Firsthand Account of His Flight," by Alan B. Shepard, Jr., Sept., 1961.

"The Moon Close Up," by Eugene M. Shoemaker, Nov., 1964. "Our Earth as a Satellite Sees It," by W. G. Stroud, Aug., 1960. "John Glenn's Three Orbits in Friendship 7," by Robert B. Voas, June, 1962. "I Fly the X-15," by Joseph A. Walker, Sept., 1962. "Countdown for Space," May, 1961; "Giant Comet Grazes the Sun," Feb., 1966; "Historic Color Portrait of Earth From Space," Nov., 1967; "Of Planes and Men," Sept., 1965; "Space Rendezvous, Milestone on the Way to the Moon," April, 1966; "Tracking America's Man in Orbit," Feb., 1962, all by Kenneth F. Weaver. "America's 6,000-Mile Walk in Space," Sept., 1965. "Extraordinary Photograph Shows Earth Pole to Pole," Feb., 1965. "School for Space Monkeys," May, 1961.

Composition for Man's Conquest of Space by National Geographic's Phototypographic Division, Herman J. A. C. Arens, Director; John E. McConnell, Manager. Printed and bound by Fawcett-Haynes Printing Corp., Rockville, Md. Color separations by Beck Engraving Co., Philadelphia, Pa.; R. R. Donnelley & Sons, Inc., Chicago, Ill.; Graphic Color Plate, Inc., Stamford, Conn.; The Lanman Co., Alexandria, Va.; Lebanon Valley Offset Co., Inc., Cleona, Pa.; and Stevenson Photocolor, Inc., Cincinnati, Ohio.

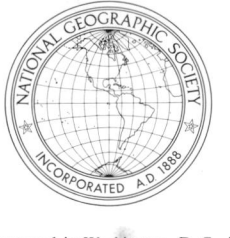

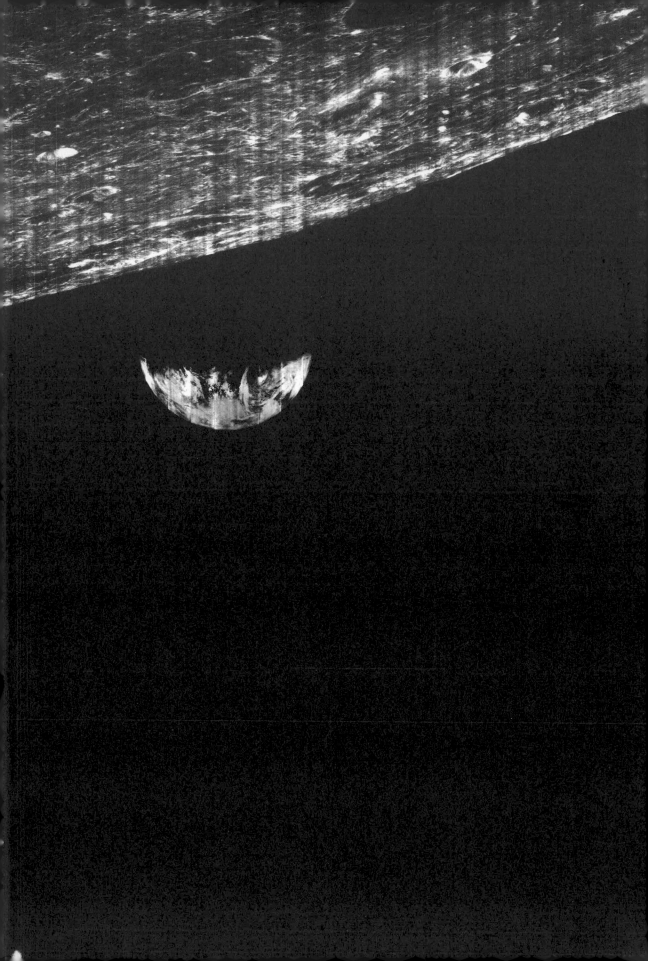